P9-DNU-047

Mark Twain Tonight!

Mark Twain Tonight!

AN ACTOR'S PORTRAIT

SELECTIONS FROM MARK TWAIN
EDITED, ADAPTED, AND ARRANGED
WITH A PROLOGUE

By HAL HOLBROOK

IVES WASHBURN, INC.

New York

COPYRIGHT © 1959 BY HAL HOLBROOK

All rights reserved, including the right to reproduce
this book, or parts thereof, in any form, except
for the inclusion of brief quotations in a review.

Library of Congress Catalogue Card Number: 59-15776

MANUFACTURED IN THE UNITED STATES OF AMERICA

8 12
H

Acknowledgment is made to Harper & Brothers for permission to quote from
Mark Twain, A Biography by Albert Bigelow Paine, copyright 1912 by
Harper & Brothers, copyright 1940 by Dora L. Paine, and from the following
works of Mark Twain:

Mark Twain's Speeches, copyright 1910 by Harper & Brothers, copyright
1938 by Clara Clemens Samossoud

Mark Twain's Speeches, copyright 1923, 1951 by The Mark Twain
Company

Mark Twain's Autobiography, copyright 1924, 1952 by Clara Clemens
Samossoud

Mark Twain's Notebook, copyright 1935 by The Mark Twain Company

Mark Twain in Eruption, edited by Bernard DeVoto, copyright 1940 by
The Mark Twain Company

Europe and Elsewhere, copyright 1923, 1951 by The Mark Twain
Company

What Is Man? and Other Essays, copyright 1917 by The Mark Twain
Company, copyright 1945 by Clara Clemens Samossoud

Chapters from My Autobiography, copyright 1906 by Harper & Brothers,
copyright 1934 by Clara Clemens Samossoud

Chapters from My Autobiography, copyright 1907 by Harper & Brothers,
copyright 1935 by Clara Clemens Samossoud

Mark Twain's Letters, copyright 1917 by The Mark Twain Company,
copyright 1945 by Clara Clemens Samossoud

Dedication

I believe it is customary to dedicate a book to one person. But after looking over the field I cannot narrow it down to one; in truth, narrowing the field down at all seems a trifle unholy. I cannot get below three and retain a quiet conscience. These three have watched my interest in Mark Twain grow from a mere seed to a bloomin' Admiration Tree.

Ed Wright, my teacher.

Ruby, my wife.

The birds that chirp at sunrise, who gave me their cheerful encouragement at many an early dawn.

Acknowledgments

This book originated with a phone call I received from John McClain, drama critic of the *New York Journal American,* on the day after the opening of *Mark Twain Tonight!* in New York. He told me that his friend Sumner Putnam of Ives Washburn, Inc., was interested in publishing the "book" of my show. I met Mr. Putnam, told him I had not written a book before, and he surprised me by remaining calm and steadfast. For Mr. Putnam's interest, faith, encouragement, and patience, I bow low.

To Lilian Lewis, my right arm during the siege, I give my heartfelt appreciation. She did the physical work of putting the manuscript on paper and the spiritual work of keeping my morale alive when the task seemed insurmountable. Her advice was invaluable, her endurance astounding. The major work on the manuscript was done during the final three weeks of my New York run.

I owe thanks, too, to Louise Fisher who assisted in the typing of the manuscript; to my wife, Ruby, who read the copy as it fell from the typewriter and offered helpful suggestions; and to James B. Pond, Mr. and Mrs. Samuel C. Webster, Dorothy Quick, Isobel Lyon, Elsie Leslie, John Winkler, and members of the Mark Twain Memorial at Hartford, all of whom provided me with information and reminiscences of Mark Twain during the past several years.

Miss Bettina Peterson and Mrs. Douglas Ryan, who performed the mysterious work of preparing the manuscript for publication, also have my gratitude and admiration.

I wish to make special acknowledgment to Professor Norman Holmes Pearson of Yale University for his advice and encouragement and to the Yale University Library for the use of quotations from newspaper reviews of Mark Twain's lectures in the *Washington Post* of November 25, 1883; the New York *Sun* of November 19, 1884; the Detroit *Free Press* of December 17, 1885; the Cleveland *Leader* of December 18, 1884; also to Professor Fred W. Lorch for his kind permission to use excerpts from the Lansing *State Republican* review of Mark Twain's lecture, published on December 21, 1871, and discovered and reprinted by Mr. Lorch in *American Literature*, Vol. 22, No. 3, November 1950.

It would be a grave oversight if I did not acknowledge the tremendous value of Caroline Thomas Harnsberger's *Mark Twain at Your Fingertips,* a gold mine of sourced selections from the whole range of his work, which led me down many a quaint back alley in the wonderland of Twain.

I wish to make grateful acknowledgment for the use of the following copyrighted matter: Harper and Brothers for excerpts from *Mark Twain's Speeches* (1910 and 1923 editions), *Mark Twain, A Biography* (1912), *Mark Twain's Letters* (1917), *What Is Man? And Other Essays* (1917), *Europe and Elsewhere* (1923), *Mark Twain's Autobiography* (1924), *Mark Twain's Notebook* (1935), *Mark Twain in Eruption* (1940), *Chapters from My Autobiography* in the *North American Review*, DC, October 5, 1906; DCX, March 1, 1907; DCXX, August 2, 1907. The Beechhurst Press, Inc., for excerpts from *Mark Twain at Your Fingertips* (1948). Charles Scribner's Sons for excerpts from *Mark Twain in Nevada* (1947). Crown Publishers for an excerpt from *The Adventures of Thomas Jefferson Snodgrass* (1928). Cyril Clemens for an anecdote in *Mark Twain—Wit and Wisdom,* Frederick H. Stokes Co., 1935. Dr. Effie Mona Mack for material from *Mark Twain in Nevada,* Charles Scribner's Sons, 1947.

Finally, I wish to acknowledge my deepest appreciation and respect to John Lotas for his courage, devotion, and unflagging determination in getting *Mark Twain Tonight!* on a New York stage.

Blissfully submitted from the beach at Sapphire Bay, St. Thomas, Virgin Islands.

HAL HOLBROOK

This book is merely a personal narrative, and not a pretentious history or a philosophical dissertation. It is a record of several years of variegated vagabondizing, and its object is rather to help the resting reader while away an idle hour than afflict him with metaphysics, or goad him with science. Still, there is information in the volume. I regret this very much, but really it could not be helped; information appears to stew out of me naturally, like the precious Ottar of Roses out of the otter. Sometimes it has seemed to me that I would give worlds if I could retain my facts; but it cannot be. The more I calk up the sources, and the tighter I get, the more I leak wisdom. Therefore, I can only claim indulgence at the hands of the reader, not justification.

—MARK TWAIN
Prefatory to *Roughing It*

Contents

Illustrations

Mark Twain Tonight!

Prologue

It began in this way. Back in early September of 1947 when my wife and I were cording up our intellectual lumber against the rigors of our final year at Denison University, the phone rang one midnight. It was the head of the Theater Department and the best man at our wedding, Ed Wright.

He said, "Hal, I have a job for you two kids when you get out of school. How would you like to tour high schools in the southwest for thirty weeks next season in your own show? I can get you $225 a week."

He told me this tale: He had been at the annual convention of the International Platform Association in Lakeside, Ohio. A school assembly booker from Dallas, Texas, Harry Byrd Kline, had said to him, "Ed, I need a dramatic attraction real bad. Do you have any kids down there at that college who could do a show for me?" Ed's mind turned over —it was generally revolving, day and night—and he assured Kline that he had just what he needed: a young married couple who had a two-person show in which they did scenes from the lives of famous personalities—Robert and Elizabeth Barrett Browning, John Alden and Priscilla, Queen Victoria and Prince Albert, Mark Twain, and some Shakespearian ones, too. He described the show in detail. It was beautifully

3

costumed, could be played on a plain stage with drapes, and would be just the thing for high school audiences. Kline said, "That's exactly what I want, Ed. I'll give them $210 for twelve shows a week, plus $15 for gas and oil, and guarantee them thirty weeks of work." Ed had the contract with him. All we had to do was sign it.

I said, "Ed, we don't have a show!"

"You can get it ready this year. I'll let you do it as an honors project. Think it over and call me back."

Ruby and I thought it over: we had no show, we had no money, no car in which to make the tour, no "beautiful costumes." But we had youth. We called Ed back and said, "We'll do it."

He gave us a copy of Mark Twain's *An Encounter with an Interviewer.* "Start with this," he said. "This is one thing you've *got* to do."

We took it home, read it, and got on the phone again.

"Are you kidding? This is the corniest thing we've ever read!"

Ed told us to work on it anyway, then show it to him. We rehearsed for a week or so, and one evening we met in an empty classroom and ran through it for him. It was pretty dreadful.

"I think I know what's wrong. You're missing the real humor of this piece. The idea here is that a man with a great sense of humor is pulling the leg of a reporter who has no sense of humor. Keep that in mind and work on it some more."

Our first performance of *An Encounter with an Interviewer* was at the Veteran's Hospital in Chillicothe, Ohio, in the suicide ward. It was a bleak place, a hopeless place. I remember the bars on the windows. Somebody played the piano, but its clattering cheerfulness was unnerving. Lonely men sat around on the scarred iron beds, on tired chairs, on the floor, staring into corners, staring at their hands, grunting in secret amusement over some vagrant thought. Somebody sang. None of those forlorn men paid any attention. A young woman social worker got up and gave us a brave introduction. She said we were college students and that we were going to create theater for them right there in front of their eyes. Nobody smiled, except me. It was a poor joke but it needed a smile just the same. Ruby and I got up in a cold sweat and started to "create theater." The men began to respond. You couldn't call it laughter. It wasn't the sort of audience response you would be likely to hear in the theater, but it was a response, and most of the sounds came after the lines which we thought were funny ourselves. When it was over there was a slight applause.

Two weeks later we did this sketch before a Kiwanis club and they laughed in the same places. We didn't know what to think.

This was my introduction to Mark Twain and the beginning of my education about him. Up to this time I knew he had written *Tom Sawyer* and *Huckleberry Finn,* but I was not sure about *Robinson Crusoe.* I began to read him and we continued to do the *Interviewer* sketch for clubs and school groups, adding other selections as we went along. We put together two of those delightful forest scenes from Shakespeare's *As You Like It,* between the young lovers, Rosalind and Orlando. We chose a whimsical episode in which young Queen Victoria comes to Prince Albert's room on the morning after their wedding and for the first time in her life watches a man shave. We constructed a scene between Robert Browning and Elizabeth Barrett Browning in which she shyly reads to him the love sonnets he has inspired. For our dramatic numbers we chose the "closet scene" between

Hamlet and his mother, and the magnificently actable selection in which Queen Elizabeth sends her lover, Essex, to his death.

It was this scene which caused the first large explosion in our married life. I had assumed the post of director of our show and one night in a small, deserted classroom on the third floor of the Science Building, I drove my wife relentlessly to achieve the emotion I felt she had to project as Elizabeth. It was only our first rehearsal of the scene. We rehearsed it over and over until we were exhausted, and then I said we must do it again. We were fairly well along with it when I stopped her to drop another critical straw upon the load she was already carrying. It was the last straw that evening. She told me off with a vehemence which Queen Elizabeth would have admired, and stormed out of the building. I followed her, guardedly, feeling very much lost and alone. Finally I came up beside her in the darkness and I saw she was crying. I felt ashamed and I put my arm around her and tried to apologize. We made up and went home. I began to learn then that there is no desolation quite so barren as the one that comes when the bond is severed between a man and his wife. It was a painful lesson, but one which I would have to learn again.

We needed three thousand dollars. In order to make the tour we would have to buy materials for costumes, some stage lights, an amplifying system for the brief musical bridges which linked our scenes together, and a station wagon to carry this cargo and us. At this point an "angel" came along, a gentleman angel by the name of Everett Reese who happened to be the president of a bank in near-by Newark, Ohio. He and his wife had observed us in the college productions, and they had taken a shine to us. Ev offered us a three-thousand-dollar loan. As far as I have been able to figure it out, we had no real collateral to offer him beyond an immature life insurance policy, and I believe he gave us the loan because he felt we were worth it. It was the sort of faith you hope will pay off.

Ev gave us the loan money eighteen months in advance of the time the full amount would be due, so that we could buy the lights, costumes, and station wagon. Our payments were to be made during the last thirty weeks of the eighteen months' term, when we would be on the tour and earning the $225 a week. We contracted to pay off $100 a week for those thirty weeks, leaving us $125 for our expenses on the road. It seemed to us a princely sum of money, but then I had never done much traveling.

We had to make our own costumes—it was too expensive to buy them. My wife was the official costume maker, but I helped, too. I want to get that in. I claim credit for the creation of the Hamlet tunic. We had no pattern, and while Ruby was an excellent seamstress, she was unfamiliar with Hamlet tunics and hesitant about starting one without some sort of a pattern to guide her. I couldn't see the difficulties. I showed her the picture in a costume book. It was nothing but a black sack with holes in it for your arms to stick through and it came down just about far enough to be discreet. I said, "All we have to do is draw this thing out on a large piece of paper, put it up next to me, trim the paper to size, lay it on top of the material, and cut it out twice; then sew the two halves together." She looked at me aghast, thought I was crazy, said it couldn't be done. I said, "Why can't it be done? Just give me some newspaper and the scissors and I'll do it myself." She gave them to me and I cut it out. We pinned the two halves together and put it on me. I looked like a thin boy in a large paper bag, so we began to chop off the excess. We finally got it trimmed down to my size, then laid the pattern on black velvet, cut it out, and sewed it up; Ruby put a lining in it and decorated it here and there with some silvery stuff and I knew we had arrived. It would not surprise me to find that this was the way they used to make them in the old days. Consider the outfit Adam made for himself, and he had no scissors.

During the Christmas vacation that year I went to New York and bought Mark Twain's wig. It was white and curly and had once been the property of Fred Stone. At the same time I had his mustache made. Ev Reese gave me one of his white linen suits which we redesigned to conform to the style worn by Mark Twain. My uncle, who is in the shoe business, secured for me a pair of slippers which looked very much like congress gaiters. I am still wearing them. It shames me to tell you that I have not been able to wear a hole in the soles after two thousand performances. My uncle shouldn't put out such good shoes.

I had based my choice of these black shoes on a picture I had acquired of Mark Twain seated in a rocking chair on the porch of his Dublin, New Hampshire, summer residence, late in life. It shows him neatly dressed in his white suit, and wearing these comfortable-looking black shoes. There is a small kitten playing at the foot of his chair. It has become one of my favorite pictures of Twain. About six years later when I began the research on my solo show I discovered that Mark Twain wore white shoes when he appeared in his white suit on the platform. By then my shoes had become familiar to me; they were a part of my characterization and I loved them. So I departed from authenticity in this case and I am still wearing my old shoes. When I put them on, Mark Twain rises up through the soles of my feet.

It was at this time, too, that I acquired the old-fashioned gold watch which I use in *Mark Twain Tonight!* It was given to me by a watchmaker in Granville, Ohio—a beautiful old gold piece which I have come to treasure. It has a winding key which you insert through the back and if you peel off two layers at the rear of it you can see into the insides. But all is quiet there, for it does not work.

The heavy watch chain and the ornate fob which hangs on it I found in my great-uncle's costume trunk. He had been an actor in the theater for about twenty years back before the turn of the century. About 1904 or '05 he got married and gave up the theater and went into the furniture business. But he kept his costume trunk. It was stored in a closet in his home for forty-five years. In the ambulance on his way to the hospital where he died, he told his wife to send me the costume trunk. When I opened it and examined the contents I was impressed by the devotion he had shown in packing them. He had been so careful to preserve everything that the materials in the costumes were still clean and strong and sound. In the tray were his wigs, sturdy and usable. His articles of make-up were arranged with patient care; and in an old-fashioned rosewood box which contained his hand properties and repertoire of spectacles, I found the watch chain and fob. From among the spectacles I chose a pair in a worn, black case and I carry them in my breast pocket.

There is one other piece of essential equipment which I have integrated into the Mark Twain solo show, and that is a small silver penknife used to cut the ends off the three cigars I smoke during a performance. This penknife came down to me from my grandfather. It is slightly bent at one end but it works very nicely. I lived with my grandfather for ten years when I was a boy and it was from my observation of him that I learned how an old man handles a cigar. I learned many other things from him, too, which I have incorporated into my characterization of Mark Twain. He was a tall man and very straight and very proud and I admired him greatly. He rose from poverty to substantial riches by virtue of his will and fortitude; he had scarcely any formal education. But he came from an era of men who did not need scholastic degrees if they were shrewd enough to profit by life's experiences. My grandfather did not look like Mark Twain, nor did he walk or talk like him, but there was about him a commanding conviction and manly integrity which I feel in the spirit of Mark Twain. My grandfather was a lonely man. When I was a boy of seven or eight I used to creep out of my bed at night and come quietly down the hall and peer at him through the archway to the living room. He would be seated in his brown armchair, often with a glass of Scotch whisky beside him, smoking his cigar. I remember that one of his hands would clench and unclench in a spasmodic way as he sat there alone, and this characteristic of his I have incorporated into my Mark Twain. My grandfather's hands were very firm and strong and on his deathbed when I went in to say good-by to him he held my hand in his so tightly that I can remember the feel of it yet.

Ruby and I started out on the high school assembly circuit in September of 1948. Our first performance was in Amarillo, Texas. In the morning we gave two shows, one at the senior high school, one at the junior high school. Then we drove forty-five miles to Claude, Texas, and gave an afternoon performance there. We were launched.

At the end of every one of those thirty weeks we spent touring down through the southwest, I wrote a long letter back to Ed Wright at Denison University, detailing the experiences we were having. He saved them all, and from them I am now able to reconstruct certain events which

characterized our journey. It was a long one. During those
thirty weeks we drove forty thousand miles and gave 307
performances. We played everything from grade schools up
to senior high schools, with an occasional college engagement thrown in. Those were our little prizes, for it was the
college audiences which seemed to enjoy our show more
than any other. It was a show which would appeal to young
and old adults more than it would to children—particularly
children who for the most part had been brought up on a
diet of Roy Rogers in the local movie houses. When we arrived at a school in one of those small southwestern towns
there would generally be a group of boys standing by the
front entrance and as we climbed out of our car they would
chant, "Oh Romeo, Romeo! wherefore art thou Romeo?" We
got used to it in time, but I don't think I ever fully adjusted
myself to the screams of derision which greeted me on my
first entrance of the show. We opened with *As You Like It*
and I wore green tights. It is not necessary to go into details.

One of the deepest scars inflicted upon my memory of
those days was a song, "Let's Say Good-by Like We Said
Hello, In a Friendly Kind of Way." It was sung by Ernest
Tubb. I do not know Ernest and I do not wish to seem un-
kind, but it is my opinion that music is not Ernest's field.
Here, of course, we deal with the question: "What is music?"
I do not feel that "Let's Say Good-by Like We Said Hello,"
etc., quite classifies. We heard it on the average of eighteen
to twenty times a day: thrice at breakfast, four times at
lunch, maybe six times during dinner; and as we clung to
each other in our hotel room at night, watching the military
maneuvers of regiment upon regiment of cockroaches, we
endured the agony of seven encores by Ernest from the
lobby below. Occasionally the pinball machine would drown
him out.

Our show sold for thirty-five dollars a performance. We kept 60 per cent of this and the other 40 per cent went to Mr. Kline, our manager. At the end of each performance we had to pack up quickly and go to the principal's office to collect our check before rushing on to our next show town. On the second day of our trip we followed this procedure and the principal handed us the thirty-five dollars in pennies, nickels, and dimes. Admission had been nine cents apiece. He insisted that we count it all, to make sure it was there. Since we had to drive forty miles to the next town and grab a quick lunch before performing there, this was disheartening. I told him I would be willing to take his word that the $35 was there; but he said, "No, I just won't feel right about that. I'll sure feel better if you just count it." I counted pennies and nickels and dimes for half an hour and the more I counted the madder I got, and the madder I got the more pennies, nickels, and dimes I dropped on the floor. I had to start over several times because I kept losing count. My mind was elsewhere. There was a running monologue going through it, all concerned with descriptions of this principal's funeral and how delighted I would be to attend it. Ruby was cheerful, so cheerful I could have strangled her. But I did not do that; I just smiled in a strained way and kept counting. Presently the thought began to come home to the principal that he had done a foolish thing and he became apologetic. This saved his life; I was on the point of digging out my Hamlet sword and exploring his machinery with it. The next day we went to a bank and counted it all over again for them. In future, I took a check or nothing.

We looked forward with much enthusiasm to our first evening engagement because we expected to have the pleasure of playing for an adult audience. We arrived at a small town on the Oklahoma panhandle where an audience of

125 had assembled to see us. Two thirds of them were children under twelve. There were two babies in their mothers' arms and a slight scattering of teen-agers in the balcony waiting for the lights to dim so they could wrestle. The older people looked as if they were attending church. Our Rosalind and Orlando scene got none of its usual laughter and Victoria and Albert did not appear to charm them. By this time the kiddies had become frightfully restless.

Our third number was to be the debut of the Elizabeth and Essex scene. Before each scene, Ruby or I gave a brief introduction from in front of the curtain, whose purpose was to give the audience the few facts they would need to follow the scene and to develop an appropriate mood for it. On this night, as I introduced Elizabeth and Essex for the first time, some instinct led me to ask the children if they would please allow the older folks in the back of the hall to hear the next number, and then "the final one would be for them, too." John Jacob Niles had worked that one rather successfully at this stop. The children assented wildly, clapping their little palms in joyful unison, and it was plain to me that they had not understood a word I said. As the scene proceeded and we tried to project our voices above the clamor, I became conscious that a lively game of hide-and-seek was in progress in and around the auditorium. Little figures kept scooting past us, and presently I noticed that two youngsters were grappling rather heatedly on the floor in front of the stage. The babies in arms tuned up and their wailing rose swiftly to an operatic crescendo. A dog joined in. When Queen Elizabeth finally sent me off to the tower that night, it seemed to me that to be beheaded was not such a bad fate, after all.

During the third week of the tour something happened in the Mark Twain number which I shall always remember.

We were giving our show in the high school in Cordell, Oklahoma, and as we started the Mark Twain selection I noticed that we were getting an unusual amount of laughter. From the very beginning we seemed to get laughs we had never been able to draw before. I sensed, vaguely, that something was amiss and as my mind clutched at possibilities I wondered if it could be my fly. The more I thought about it the more I knew that it *must* be my fly. I sat down in the armchair and the hysteria out front mounted higher. That seemed to settle it. The question was—should I look down? I knew that if I looked down and it was open, and the audience knew *I* knew it was open, we would simply have to close the curtain and end the show. I looked over at Ruby and saw that she was in high spirits and careening along in the role of interviewer with no knowledge of the abyss which lay before us. She had that light in her eye which an actor always gets when a scene is going beautifully, a look of excited satisfaction. I groaned inwardly at the realization of the size of the shock she was in for, and then I looked down at my fly. It was gaping. For a moment I had a wild desire to laugh myself but checked it. The audience was drowning us out now and I could see that the thought had come to Ruby that maybe it wasn't our acting, after all. She was worried, but bore bravely on. There seemed no polite way out; I looked down again and in Mark Twain's slow drawl said, "By George, I've gone and left my fly wide open." Then I buttoned it up. Gales of laughter rent the auditorium, fore and aft. Rows of students bent double and did slow rolls to the floor. My mouth twitched horribly and behind the blessed disguise of the mustache I began to laugh, too.

Ruby had been considerably slowed down by this unrehearsed commentary. It was like watching one of those movies where someone dives off the high board and they stop the film and let that person hang there awhile, and then back up. She bent forward and inspected me closely and I saw her begin to turn red, then white, and then go a little toward the blue shade, a startling patriotic effect. Presently she regained character, arose from her chair with a magnificent display of dignity, and stalked off stage. But she did not remain in character all the way. She began to go into convulsions before she struck the wings and I could hear her shrieking with laughter as she pleaded with the boy on the curtain to "pull," "pull," "pull!" To this day, the last thing I do before going on stage is check my fly.

During the fifth week of our tour we did fifteen shows and drove 950 miles in five days, much of it on dirt roads and through the mountains. We were getting the smiles wiped off our faces in double-quick time. In the middle of the week we crossed over into Arkansas and played Mena, the home of Lum and Abner. They liked us so much that after the show we had to beg two boys to carry out our heavy costume trunks to the car. On Wednesday of that week we had a show at nine o'clock in the morning, one at 2:00 P.M., and another at eight in the evening, all in different towns. For the eight o'clock show we had a record-breaking evening crowd of 150. On Thursday we played Fort Smith, Arkansas, in the morning, and then drove to a tiny place called Alma, where we played afternoon and evening shows in the same hall. Alma was very nice to us. Some of the kids came back for a second dose in the evening. Many of them had come from way up in the hills, children who never got to see much of anything in the entertainment line, and it surprised us to find them so well behaved and friendly and perceptive. Even the school superintendent treated us with respect and that made us feel warm all over. At this point we had done thirteen shows in four days, but the friendly reception we received at Alma renewed our spirits.

There were two shows to give on Friday, the second at B――――. The school was poor. The auditorium was also the gymnasium, a bare, scarred wooden affair. When the bell for the assembly period rang we heard the stampede of children entering the arena and saw that many of them were from the grade school. We pleaded with the superintendent to seat these youngsters on the sides or at the back and allow the older students to sit forward where they might be able to enjoy the show. He refused. It was a massacre. Little children leaned over the front edge of the stage and others perched high up on window sills and chattered like squirrels in a tree. We tried to be heard above the commotion, but it was an impossible situation. By this time we had learned to take things a little more philosophically, so we simply did our show as best we could.

When it was over, Ruby and I were directed to report to the superintendent's office. We got out of our costumes and packed our trunks and went to his office. There was another man there who looked as if he might be the football coach, and I had the feeling as we entered that they had been talking about us. They did not look friendly. The superintendent began by saying,

"That was a bad show you gave us. I don't think we should pay you."

I asked him what, in particular, he had disliked about the show.

"I didn't see it," he said. "Mr. ―――― here did, though, and he says you didn't try hard enough."

"We did try, but nobody would listen to us."

"That's not our fault. It's up to you to make them listen."

"That's true," I said. "But with an audience where the ages range from six to eighteen, it helps to have a little discipline.

There weren't even any teachers out there. It was a mad-house."

"Our teachers are too busy to go to assemblies. They have other things to do."

"I can understand that. But your students won't listen."

The coach broke in. "We had a magician here last week and they listened to him. It was that stuff from Shakespeare. You should have left that out. You don't deserve to be paid for giving us a show like that."

"Other schools seem to enjoy it."

"Well, our kids don't."

"Very well, you needn't pay us."

The superintendent said, "We'll pay you. We just want you to know we don't think you're worth $35. But don't worry, I won't tell your manager about this. We'll just keep it to ourselves."

"Please *do* tell him. I want him to know about these things, so that we won't have to play these grade school audiences."

"Don't worry, I won't tell him."

"I want you to. He knows what kind of a show we have and respects it. I would be delighted to have you write him."

"We don't do things like that around here. We won't tell on you."

We climbed into our car and started off. Suddenly we both began to cry. Five weeks of frustration—of battling audiences which were so often unprepared for us, of driving at breakneck speeds over uneven roads to make engage-ments, of wanting to do our best and falling short of it because there were so many obstacles in the way—the ac-cumulation of all this gathered up inside of us and got loose and we broke down and cried out our frustration, and then drove to the next town. In my letter to Ed of October 16,

1948, I described this experience and how we felt about it and then wound up with this paragraph:

Well, that's show business—I'll say it again. I guess the most difficult part of this tour is this: we give everything, the audience gives nothing unless they like it, and in the meantime they act as rudely as they like toward us. It's a wonderful proving ground for the development of our characters—but is it for the development of our talents, whatever they may be? We have a good show. But is this the place for it?

Looking back on it now, almost twelve years later, I think perhaps it was. Talent is not a rare thing. But the will to use it and the technique which gives it form are not so easy to acquire. It takes a good deal of humiliation to make a success, just as it takes a good deal of living to understand why this must be so.

We went south for the first time in our lives. We drove down to Helena, Arkansas, on the banks of the Mississippi River, and did a performance there. Then we took the ferryboat at Helena and crossed the river. It was my first ride on a ferryboat and I went up on the top deck and watched the old pilot standing in front of the great wheel and imagined Mark Twain in a pilothouse many years ago. Then I got an idea. I had been reading that Mark Twain had a unique way of walking. It was described as a "shuffling gait" or a "kind of duck waddle." I walked up and down the side deck of the ferryboat and tried for the "feel" of it. I noticed that the deck was very slightly canted to allow water to drain off, I suppose. I noted that if I relaxed and walked "with the deck" there was a tendency to throw the weight on the outboard foot which gave me a sort of list to starboard or port, depending on which direction I was going. That's how I found my walk for Mark Twain. Nearly ten years later

I saw the Thomas Edison film of Twain and when he walked toward the camera the "list" was there.

As we drove down through Mississippi into the Southland we began to develop our first impressions of that unique section of the country. Some of the sights we saw were discouraging—old wooden shanties which no life seemed to inhabit, until you saw the tenants out in the cottonfields, stooping low, dragging a long bag behind them through dirty white rows of ripe cotton. Then we came upon some plantation mansions—gracious houses, rich with tradition and looking for all the world as they had in *Gone with the Wind*, and, incidentally, creating a weird contrast with the surrounding poverty of dirty, weather-wrecked shacks. Negroes lived there—or rather, they existed. We saw the chain gang working on the roads in Mississippi, black faces and hands showing out of striped canvas suits. We had never seen these sights before, only read of them. We were in the heart of the biggest cotton-producing counties in the world.

The most compelling example of racial discrimination we saw on our trip was this: a signboard in East Prairie, Missouri, with the town's World War II Honor Roll printed on it—the names of all the men who had served their country and in some cases died for it; that is, died for freedom and democracy. It was a long list and a large billboard, but on one wing of the board there was a separate list and in large black letters, at the head of this particular column was printed the word: COLORED.

On November 4 we played Central High School in Little Rock, Arkansas. I remember the stage there. They told us that it was one of the largest in the country and they were very proud of that.

Out of the $125 a week which remained after the payments on our loan, we were able to save about twenty.

That is, if we were lucky. If we had a flat tire, or if the car needed repair, our small savings were swept away. We had to save something to live on during the three week hiatus over the Christmas vacation, when we would have no work. So our pennies were precious to us and we ate and slept in the cheapest places we could find. By early December we had managed to save only about $150 to cover the three weeks. The tremendous speeds at which we were forced to drive and the rugged road surfaces we traveled raised havoc with our tires and we seemed to be constantly replacing rim-cut tubes. And one day, in early December, passing through the town of Colgate, Oklahoma, on a fast jump between two dates, we drove slowly alongside a long funeral procession which was occupying the center of the wide main street. We were looking for our route turn-off, but when we found that it was on the other side of the funeral line we pulled over to the side of the road and waited for the procession to pass. At that moment, two deputies strode up, hauled us into court, and the city manager socked us with a $15.50 fine.

That afternoon we saw a state highway patrolman and stopped to ask him about the existence of a law against passing funerals in Oklahoma. He said, "There is none." We explained to him what had happened to us in Colgate and he shook his head. "We have been trying to stop that," he said. "It's a sort of a poor town nowadays; used to be some coal mines around there but they petered out. They split that fine up amongst themselves. I'm sorry you had this trouble."

In my letter of December 4 to Ed Wright describing this incident, I ended the story with this: "Really, I think I could write a book after this tour, if I had all these letters together where I could go over them. I'd send my first copy to Colgate! A signed edition, $15.50 a copy."

We spent Christmas in California that year, in Hollywood, where my older sister was living. We rented a motel room for $2.50 a night and ate only two meals a day, one of them at my sister's, and thus we survived the period of unemployment. As Christmas approached I began to wonder what I could get Ruby in the way of a present, funds being so low. I knew she needed a new dress badly, but she had not mentioned it. On the evening before Christmas we passed a small dress shop which was advertising a close-out sale, lease expiring, and so on. I pulled her inside and had her try on a few dresses in the hope that she might find something in that store she would like and which would not cost much money. She found a very pretty green, two-piece dress which looked lovely on her. It had been cut way down to $19.95, but that still seemed too much for our pocketbook, so we left without taking it. We walked down the street and then stopped. I said, "Ruby, I'm going to try to bargain with that man for the dress." She looked at me with interest because she knew I had never had the courage to do that sort of thing before.

We returned to the store and found the manager, and I began to palaver. He knocked off $2.50. We took the dress over to my sister's apartment and laid it reverently under the tree.

In California we met a man who at that time was the czar of the school assembly circuits in the West. He lived in a sumptuous home and when we were ushered into his office by an aide he was seated behind a large, ornate desk, looking for all the world like a man who thought he could buy anything. He wanted us to tour for him the following year and when we told him that we were not going to do any more school assembly tours, that in future we would try for higher-fee dates at colleges and women's clubs, he became sarcastic. "You strike me as a couple of kids with big ideas. What you need is several years on the school assembly circuits before you can hope to try for something better. If you'll take my advice, you'll let me book you next year for thirty-five weeks and trim your show down so that you can do it twenty times a week." We declined.

Throughout the winter, we played the west Texas and eastern New Mexico areas, often driving through snow and on ice to make our shows. One day we received word that an attraction traveling our circuit, a trio of girl singers, had been struck by a butane truck while driving on icy roads in New Mexico and had been killed. It was a sobering thought. We learned what a "dry norther" was in Texas lingo—it is a helluva storm without snow. A "blue norther" dumps a lot of snow on you to boot. There is a good deal of weather in Texas, along with everything else. I recall one headline in the Abilene paper that year: SNOW, SLEET, RAIN, FOG, DUST, AND FLOODS DEAL STATE LOW BLOW.

The motels in that part of the country had little gas heaters, but often during the blizzards the gas supply ran low and those heaters had about the same efficiency as four match flames confronting an iceberg. Some nights we piled everything on the beds we could find, including our extra clothes, and crawled under the mess and hoped for a thaw. In the morning, preparing for an eight-thirty show, our dressing rooms in the schools were freezing and when we unpacked our costumes they appeared to have a frost on them. If the heat in the radiator was up we would warm them over that; or if such luxury items as radiators were not available we waved a match over them a few times to take the chill off. It was an invigorating life, standing nearly naked in some of those dressing rooms with the temperature about ten degrees. The only advantage we could locate was that it was too cold for cockroaches.

Occasionally we would lose dates when the schools were closed because of blizzard conditions or we might have to juggle others and then there would always be a mile-a-minute ride between them, in order to fit them in. On one day in February we played four shows and drove over three hundred miles. Occasionally we would suffer deep depressions for reasons we could not seem to understand—the long pull, the discouragements, the difficult weather and driving conditions, and the constant and tremendous drain upon our energies took its toll. Our emotions were very often near the surface and when someone was kind to us we had to fight back tears of gratitude.

I remember a principal at the high school in Cisco, Texas. We had a fine performance there and a very appreciative audience and after the performance the principal came up on the stage and grasped our hands and made the loveliest speech. He said, "You know, we've had a lot of programs at this high school, but I think everyone here will agree that this is the finest of them all, and we want to thank you young artists for coming to our school. . . ." He had called us "artists." We were very touched. We had been very depressed for a week or so, but this man's thoughtfulness at just that moment turned the tide. When we drove away from his school we felt glad to be alive again.

Spring finally came. We saw it in east Texas. The countryside reminded us of Ohio in some respects, for there were so many trees; pines mostly, but the greenery gave us the sense of home. We celebrated the arrival of spring by putting on a new scene, this one from *Macbeth*. Ruby worked for weeks to make the costumes, gathering pieces of material in the small towns and working on them at night. We rehearsed in our motel rooms. When the walls were thin, the occupants in the adjoining rooms must have sat bolt upright in their beds when Ruby wailed: "Yet who would have thought the old man to have had so much blood in him?"

We stayed at one hotel in Texas which I shall always remember. We drove into this town late one night and the only rooms available were in a hotel that was so ancient and unsteady that it leaned toward you. An old character with a stiff leg ushered us up the three ghoulish flights to the room, dragging his leg behind him like an anchor, and opened the door. I just stood and looked at it, looked at the peeling paper and water stains on the walls, and the cockroach colony at work and play in the far corner, and I tried to say something. No words would come. The old fellow sensed that some conversational item was in order, so he pointed a thorny finger at the bathroom. "Mighty convenient, those toilets," he said. "Right nice things to have so nice and close." I agreed that a close toilet had merits over a distant one, and I noted mentally that such a choice property must be mute testimony that this was a "better-type room."

"Yep, mighty convenient," he continued, in a slow, wormy drawl. "And since I'm right here I think I'll just take a turn at her." He did, and left the room with an air of peace and satisfaction.

During the final week of our thirty on tour we were marooned in a flood in Alice, Texas. We managed to salvage all but one of the dates by some frantic juggling of the schedule. Then we set out for New York. The year before, on a visit to New York, we had auditioned for an old-time agent by the name of Chamberlain Brown. During our year on tour he had written us several times, offering us the sky and the stars at a very slight charge. We did not really believe his promises but when he offered to organize an audition for us in early May and invite "the leading producers of the theater" to see us, we were in no position to turn him down. If only one producer showed up, it might be worth the trip. Chamberlain's letters to us ran over with confidence that this was going to be our big break. He described the distinguished audience he was assembling and our hopes rose in spite of ourselves.

We finished our last school assembly performance and drove from near Corpus Christi to New York in three days. The audition was held in a radio studio on the north end of Times Square and we shared the rental expense. Our audience consisted of six persons: three friends, an old character actress, a young actor who had nowhere to go that night, and Chamberlain Brown. This was our wide-eyed introduction to the disappointments an actor seeking work in the New York theater must be prepared to face.

Chamberlain Brown died about five years ago. He was a legend in the theater, a familiar name to every actor who "made the rounds." With his brother, Lyman, he occupied an office which was musty with the antiquity of tradition. The walls were papered with old posters and programs, the furniture was bent with age, the litter of years and years of occupancy overcame you when you entered the museum. It was impossible to believe that a dust rag had passed over anything there within forty years. I never saw but one shirt on Chamberlain, a faded blue one with the sleeves cut off at the elbows. Yet this was the one agent's office in New York where an actor was never sent away without some word of encouragement. The encouragement was often as fantastic as the place itself, but many an actor made this his last stop at the end of a weary day of tramping the streets and Chamberlain always sent him away with the hope that success was just around the corner.

I have added this last paragraph because a strange thing happened a moment ago. I have been writing for two days without sleep to finish this book. At two o'clock, as I completed my revisions through the story of Chamberlain's memorable audition, I fell asleep. The phone awoke me at five. It was his brother, Lyman, calling to tell me how happy he was over my success. I have not spoken to him in five years.

After our year on the school assembly circuit Ruby and I graduated to the women's clubs and the smaller colleges. For the next three years we toured together from late September until late May and did four to six more weeks on the road during the summers. We finished out the summers by acting in stock companies.

The women's clubs enjoyed our show and were very gracious to us; but the audience response at the colleges was more fun. Their response was often huge—they caught every fly ball and grounder we hit out to them and returned it with a laugh. The game of playing with audience laughter, of urging it along with a look or a movement and measuring pauses so as to gain the greatest effect, has given me some exhilarating moments on the stage. In my opinion, there are few joys in life so satisfying as the pleasure of hearing a rightly timed pause pay off with a burst of laughter. At this point in my development as an actor I was not much concerned with the *thought* a laugh can provoke. *Getting* the laugh was sufficient.

Two of the friends who attended our Chamberlain Brown audition were James B. Pond, the son of Mark Twain's lecture manager and editor of *Program* magazine, and his associate, Agnes McTernan. They were to become two very important people to us and the source of much valuable information and encouragement.

Ruby and I went to "Bim" Pond's office on the day after the audition and he talked to me about Mark Twain. He had known him as a boy and his father had brought home many impressions of Twain. I asked him to tell me how Mark Twain had talked, what his voice had sounded like. Bim leaned back in his chair and began to drawl: "Pond, when I enga-a-ged you to send me out on the ... public highway ... with all the other ba-a-ndits ... there was nothing in our contract which sta-a-ted that I would have to sta-a-nd on cold railway pla-a-tforms ... in the middle of the night ... waiting for tra-ains that never ca-a-me!"

Bim Pond, himself, is an interesting man, a unique man, and there is something of him in my characterization of Mark Twain. Bim's wit is pointed and even savage sometimes. There seems to be a large amount of disillusionment in him and when he cannot contain it I have seen people frightened by it. At times it has frightened me. When his father died he took over the lecture business and developed it to a point of pre-eminence in the field. He booked the greatest names in the concert and lecture field; it was he who started Ruth Draper upon her matchless career. In time, other managers invaded the lecture field and many of his artists deserted him. I believe this hurt him very deeply. One day he went to his office, read his mail, then walked out of the office, and locked the door. He never went back.

I admire him. He is a man of opinions and fearless about expressing them. He is a wonderful speaker with a bagful of stories and a masterful way of telling them. But it is the shrouded hurt I sense in him and his manliness in attempting to hide it which draws me to him. He is much like Twain in this respect. He often refers to himself as having "been dead for twenty years." But he is not; there is a lion in him which will not be chained down and he transmits to me the character of an era. I think of Bim when I am telling the story of Captain Sellers in Act Three.

My memories of those years on the road are filled with many impressions which may seem to have nothing to do with acting or my association with Mark Twain. But they were a part of the plan. I remember driving, driving miles and miles, often at night. Sometimes we would finish a show and then get into the car and drive a hundred miles or more to the next town. It was our way of working off the excitement of a performance. We saw so much of the country, and I have tender memories of it by moonlight. Often we did not talk. There is a sense of loneliness which night seems to bring. The mind floats far afield. I remember our headlights probing the roads we traveled. I remember how glorious it was when we crossed the prairies under a full sky of stars, and how heavenly the landscape is when it is under the silver spell of moonlight, and how when the weather was warm and the car windows could be left open the scent of the country rushed in and carried with it memories of youth and the mysteries of the strange places we were passing through. I got a sense of the beautiful bigness of the country, and of the importance of the land itself: the trees, the red clay, the ripe fields of grass and wheat and corn, and, above all, the covering sky. I remember mornings when we had to rise too early and hit the road before the sun had started up. As we swept along I could see the country waking up, the lights going on, the first stirring of families on the farms, the men coming out and walking to barns.

I remember once in Oklahoma watching an endless freight

train crossing the prairie as the sun came up beyond it. It moved lazily across the rim of the prairie and suddenly I got such an urgent sense of the oneness of this country, of the ties that bind its riches together. I thought: that freight will cross the country from end to end, gathering upon it the soil of the regions it passes through, blending this into a mixture of America. It will change its personnel from time to time, so that the engineer from Ohio might say to his replacement in Denver, "Hi, Ralph, it's all yours the rest of the way." A simple thought—but there was something wonderful about it that early in the morning.

It seems to me that the most God-like thing I know is nature. In the sky I see eternity, but in the land I see the source and harvest of life—life which stretches back to the dawn and will go on into a darkness I shall never see. I feel the motherhood of land; the generosity of her giving, the bounty of her sustenance. We bleed the land for our needs, we ravage her treasures and deface her nobility; but her gifts are deeply bedded and her very scars breed further bounty for other men. There is about the land a relentless passivity of spirit that we cannot quench, and in the face of it the mere seventy-odd years allotted to the life span of man shrinks to meagre and tiny consequence. Death can blot us out so quickly.

I felt the breath of it once. It was in January of our fourth year on the road, just after I had changed partners. Ruby was home, expecting our first child, Victoria. She had toured with me until the fifth month of her pregnancy, finishing just before Christmas with a trip to her native Newfoundland, where we played three towns. Then we had gone to New York and auditioned for her replacement. We chose a young actress named Lee Firestone and she took over Ruby's roles for the remainder of the season.

Lee and I completed our swing through the south at Mathiston, Mississippi, on a Saturday night. We had to begin the next leg of our tour on Monday evening in Dumas, Texas, 950 miles away. I carefully figured the timing for this trip and decided that if we could keep our speed at eighty miles per hour most of the way we would arrive in Dumas on Monday afternoon, in time to set up the show. When we left Mathiston early Sunday morning it was raining hard.

I had learned to dread wet roads as much as icy ones on these fast jumps. On several occasions before I had experienced the helplessness which comes when a car begins to glide on its own, when life goes out of the steering wheel. I kept the speedometer at eighty and watched the road for possible signs of danger. We crossed the Mississippi River into southern Arkansas, made a sharp right turn, then a turn to the left and started up the long incline of a railroad viaduct. As we came over the top of it I saw the road stretching straight ahead of us, its surface freshly black-topped and smooth. I checked the speedometer and it was nearing eighty. When we came off the viaduct and leveled out I noticed some gravel on the road ahead, thrown out by a farm vehicle entering upon the highway, I supposed. There was only a little of it and I did not slacken speed. As we passed over it, the life went out of the wheel and the car began to drift slowly to the left. Lee was asleep on the seat beside me. I glanced at the shoulders on each side of the road. They appeared to be about four feet wide before they dropped off sharply into gullies about six feet deep. The mud looked soft with rain and where it met the new road surface there was a sharp drop of several inches. I took my foot off the gas pedal so the engine drag would slow us, gradually.

When it looked as if we were going off the left side of the

road, I shifted the wheel slightly to the right and promptly the car changed course and drifted in that direction. This had all happened in the space of four or five seconds and the falling mileage needle was still above sixty. I figured that if I could keep the car pointed straight ahead until the two wheels on the right side dropped off the pavement, I could then apply the brakes, using the soft mud as traction, and slow us down enough to give us a chance at survival. I held the wheel with my left hand and reached out with the other one to support Lee, who was still asleep. At the instant the wheels slid off onto the shoulder and I felt a tremendous tug on the steering wheel. It shivered violently in my hand and shook my whole body the way a bulldog would shake a cat, if he could get hold of one. I applied the brakes, slowly at first, then with desperate urgency as the wheel tore away from my hand. We began to nose over and Lee woke up. The car was describing a slow arc with the right front wheel at its base—it was the nearest thing to one of those carnival rides I can remember, the kind where you swing up and roll over. I remember sitting behind the wheel during that somersault and wondering what it was going to feel like when we came down. We landed squarely on the roof with a sickening S-C-R-U-N-C-H and my head hit bottom on the ceiling.

After the impact it was very still. I heard the wheels whirring around, the rain pouring steadily down and that was all. I thought, "I'm alive!" Then I thought, "I wonder if Lee is, too." There was a long pause before I could get her name out.

"Lee."

A week or two went by—then:

"Hal."

"Are you all right?"

"I think so. Are you?"

"Yes, I think so."

I moved my arms and legs and they all worked. My head hurt, but nothing felt broken in it. Lee said, "I think I'm all right. Can you open your door?"

I groped around for the door handle but could not get my bearings. I was sitting behind the wheel, resting on my head, and my sense of direction was gone.

"I can't find it."

"Try the window. My door won't open."

Again I tried to locate the handle but my co-ordination was all out of kilter. I suppose it was shock.

"Lee, I can't get hold of it. Can you find yours?"

She found it, of course. Women always do at moments like that. We had a *Life* magazine on the seat between us and she laid it out on the soft mud for a doormat. We crawled out. The rain soaked us thoroughly before we had time to stand up. We sloshed through the mud and up the side of the gully to the road, and we stood on that highway and looked one way and then looked the other. It was deserted. Then we looked at the car. Steam was rising from it. The wheels were still turning slowly, and the rain beat steadily down on it. We looked at each other. Suddenly the impact of our glorious good fortune overcame us and we threw our arms around each other.

About five or ten minutes later a car came by and stopped. Its occupant was eager to know all about the accident. He seemed almost to enjoy the details even more than we had. The next town was about fifteen miles up the road, so Lee climbed into his truck to get help and I stayed on the road and waited. Cars came by and all of them stopped, and all of them wanted the full story. Everyone asked if someone had been hurt and when I said, "No," they seemed disappointed and left. I waited in the rain for about forty-five minutes. Finally the tow truck came. Its owner flipped our station wagon over as neatly as you would flip a pancake, and then towed us into town. He called a friend in to help and they worked all day that Sunday. They pushed the radiator forward, straightened the fenders so the wheels could turn, and pried up the body frame to allow one door to open. Every window in the station wagon had been shattered except the front ones. The top had been squashed down to where there was only a few inches of clearance between my head and the ceiling. The interior of the car was covered with mud. Mud had somehow gotten inside our trunks and most of Lee's dresses were badly soiled.

The car was ready about four thirty in the afternoon and we climbed in and started for Texas. We drove all night and all the next day, wiring ahead to the committee chairman in Dumas to explain what had happened and begging him to have everything ready for us when we arrived. We arrived about five fifteen and went directly to the High School auditorium—it was locked and there was not a soul in sight. We spent a precious half hour locating the chairman and by this time I was not looking forward to giving a performance. We were exhausted, of course, and the lack of preparation had given us a bad opinion of the audience before it arrived. When it did arrive, we were surprised at the size of it. The town was small but it seems to me we had eight or nine hundred people packed into that auditorium. They turned out to be a wonderfully responsive crowd and our resentment melted away under the warmth of it. It was an exciting show. Afterward we were given a fine dinner by the chairman and his friends and the whole evening turned out to be very pleasant, indeed.

Our schedule gave us no time to have the car repaired, so

we filled our engagements in the southwest and headed for
southern California in a vehicle which bore all the marks of
an Okie land cruiser. We created quite a stir in southern
California. People stopped on the street to observe us as we
went by. Many advised us to junk it. In Hollywood, where
we played a fashionable women's club, I began to feel shame-
faced about it. I suppose we could have had it washed, but
why? The top was bashed in, the windows on three sides
were shattered, the fenders were wrinkled up, and assorted
dents decorated other areas. I thought it looked romantic;
but the southern Californians did not. I guess it goes to
show how far the civilization of southern California has
come since the days when the Overland Stage and the wagon
trains carried the ancestors of those people out there. We got
the car repaired in Omaha six weeks later. The insurance
company paid the bill—$850.00—and then said good-by to
me forever.

The following year Ruby and I moved to New York with
our infant daughter, and I set forth upon the pavements to
try to find work in radio, television, or theater. After four
years of professional partnership with my wife, it was now
necessary for me to find work alone. It was about this time
that the idea first began to form in my mind for creating a
solo show around the character of Mark Twain. It remained
an idea for another year.

Meanwhile, I began to read Twain more seriously, to take
a fresh interest in finding out what made him tick. I had
been doing Twain in the *Interviewer* sketch for four years
but creating him alone on the stage was another matter. It
was a frightening thought, too, because I had never done
any solo work in my life. In fact, I had always been afraid
to stand on my feet and talk. In cases where I had to make

even the briefest speech I had always failed miserably. It seemed that the minute I stood up all the things I had planned to say fled right out of my mind and I stumbled along in the most awkward and embarrassing fashion, and finally sat down in disgrace. The prospect of standing alone on the stage for an hour or more was terrifying. But something drove me to go ahead with the idea. Perhaps I just wanted to prove to myself that I could do it.

Or, perhaps the real motivation was Ed Wright. He had a program of hilarious solo sketches and I had often accompanied him when he went out to neighboring towns to fill engagements. His sense of timing was beautiful to watch— it still is—and I got to studying the audiences at these places and thinking what a joy it would be if I could make people laugh like that. Ed used the pause with devastating effect and that is where I first acquired my admiration for it.

He had one sketch which was a favorite of mine, as it is with all his audiences. In this one he plays the part of a young man with the astounding name of Elmer Wartz. Elmer has won the hog-calling contest of the state of Indiana and has come home to find himself famous. The sketch concerns his acceptance speech at a banquet in his honor. For the character Ed wears a carrot-colored fright wig and the most beautiful set of buck teeth that ever hopped out of a dentist's office. But I noticed that he never gave the teeth away too soon. He waited. He got the audience started along, and when he had the merriment built up to where he wanted it, he smiled. Slowly. It just seemed to spread those teeth from one ear to the other. I have watched audiences laugh until the tears ran down their cheeks at that sketch; and two years ago, when I saw it again, it was as funny to me as it was the first time. It is broad comedy, but there is great artfulness in it.

I started to build the solo show in the fall of 1953. By this time another friend of ours, Nancy Wells, had taken over Ruby's spot in the two-person show and we were filling a few engagements around New York just to keep ourselves alive. I could see that the two-person affair was not going to carry me much further. But acting jobs in New York were hard to find—harder than I had expected. I did a few small things here and there, but mostly it was just an uphill job, whose chief feature was walking from one office to another and trying to get to say hello to somebody who might give me work.

One illustration should suffice to describe the difficulties I had to face. Shortly after my arrival in New York I applied for an interview with the man who was casting the Sunday night Philco and Goodyear Playhouse series on television. Eight months and many post cards later I was given an appointment. I was admitted to a carpeted room with a modernistic desk in the center of it. The man told me to sit down and tell him about myself. I told him about the show Ruby and I had toured around the country and showed him our circular, which I had thought quite handsome. It cost enough to be handsome, anyway. He glanced at it, flipped it over, then tossed it aside. He said, "Do you get paid for that?"

This kind of disinterest has always unnerved me, so I began to think again about the idea of doing a solo show in the character of Mark Twain. I consulted my friend "Bim" Pond and got from him copies of several of Mark Twain's lecture programs, showing the selections he had used on the platform. "An Encounter with an Interviewer" was always there; also "The Italian Guide" episode from *The Innocents Abroad*, "The Golden Arm Ghost Story," "The Jumping Frog," the "King Sullerman" episode from *Huckleberry Finn*, the German language burlesque from *A Tramp Abroad*, and the "Ram" story from *Roughing It*. I went around to the secondhand book stores and hunted for out-of-print editions of Mark Twain's books and speeches and began to pore through them. Ideas for selections I could use in a solo show began to take shape.

The first thing I began to work on was "The Italian Guide" scene. Once I found from my research that Mark Twain had acted out some of his selections, taking the individual parts, the show began to look more interesting to me and more fun. One of my biggest problems from the very beginning was to establish the character of Mark Twain firmly and then to work out a technique of portraying other characters, such as the Guide, for instance, through the character of Mark Twain—a sort of double impersonation.

The technique I settled upon is this: I first create the "character" to be played in the episode—such as the Guide, or Huck, or Jim. Once I feel I have conceived one of these characters properly I do him again and *think* Mark Twain. The voice quality immediately changes when I do that and the physical movements acquire a different pace and quality. It took a good deal of practice but in time I was able to come up with the illusion that I was Mark Twain doing these various people, not Hal Holbrook. It is like straining soup through a sieve: all the vitamins and minerals get through, but the egg noodles remain.

The most difficult scene on the show (and the most rewarding to me) is the episode from *Huckleberry Finn* in which "Mark Twain" plays Huckleberry describing the shooting of Boggs and the attempted lynching of Colonel Sherburn. There are eight different characters in that. It requires a good deal of vocal gymnastics.

The character of Mark Twain has come upon me slowly. I am always learning something new about him and it shifts the emphasis of the characterization in one direction or another. At first I studied pictures, all the pictures I could find. Twain was very relaxed in front of the camera, or appeared to be, and he is shown in a great variety of poses. Certain characteristics were repeated: his stance, which has the eager quality of the prow of a ship; the forward jutting of his head and a habit of seeming to peer *down* at you, not up; the placing of his hands on his hips, palms out; a solemn countenance lit by the mischievous glint in his eye; the unmistakable quality of "presence" which characterizes a man who is used to center stage and enjoys it. All these qualities and mannerisms come through to me in his pictures, these, and a spirit of brooding sadness—deep and hidden—but still there. In some rare photographs it shows with eloquent clarity.

I found some examples of how he had introduced himself— he disliked being introduced by effusive program chairmen and preferred to "do the act" himself. His methods charmed me. Sometimes he would come out on stage and begin to introduce the "speaker of the evening" and it would turn out to be he himself. Then he might throw in a few compliments aimed at himself, which seemed to me an ideal way to introduce Mark Twain because it showed that he was willing to poke fun at himself, a technique which has always been popular with humorists, right up to Jack Benny.

I sought for a symbol which the audience could readily identify with Mark Twain. The cigar was a natural choice. I had found some humorous commentary on his smoking habits and it was at this point that I decided upon using the cigar. To my knowledge Mark Twain never actually smoked during a lecture, but the cigar serves a dual purpose for me. First, it helps to establish Mark Twain's eccentricity as a lecturer. From my reading and research I discovered that he

was considered a unique platform personality in his day—
that his technique of casual delivery and lounging about the
stage shocked and surprised audiences at first, then gradually
charmed them. In Twain's day it was customary for a lecturer to stand still in the middle of the stage, looking pretty
much straight ahead, and deliver his oration. Twain's method,
as described in newspaper reviews which I found in the Yale
Library, was this:

He came in with his head forward and looked like a man who
had lost something on the stage and wasn't exactly sure that he
would be able to find it . . . he faced the audience with a puzzled,
careworn expression, as if he had met the people before, but
couldn't just at the moment recall their names. His half closed
eyes appeared to peer out from under the bushy eyebrows with
a puzzled gaze that had been regarding life seriously for forty
odd years, and couldn't quite make it out. . . . He told his stories
with that inimitable Down East drawl of his and took his audience into his confidence with a serious unconventionality that
was most delightful. . . . He also reminds you of someone you
have seen before, you can't tell who, but you are friends with him,
for old acquaintance sake, from the first.*

I like all that. But did you notice the "Down East drawl"
business? You see the trouble you can get into by too much
research? Nearly everybody describes his drawl as "western"
or "southern" or "Missouri." The Missouri we can rule out,
because it had only become a state a few years before he
moved there and all the inhabitants came from Virginia and
Tennessee and Kentucky and places like that, and they all
brought their drawls with them. This research business is
enlightening in more ways than one. It isn't so much what
you put in as it is what you leave out.

* Detroit *Free Press*, December 17, 1885.

But let us be scholars and march forward again:

"While his audience roared with delight he simply pulled at his moustache and scowled." *

That wouldn't work so well these days. It's been done too often since 1884; so I avoid it.

"When Mark Twain walked on the stage . . . [wearing] his discouraged expression of countenance, he was welcomed with a prolonged clapping of hands. Without apparently recovering his spirits, he sauntered to the reading desk, felt for it with his right hand, found it, and began." †

I tried this a few times, but failed to get the humor of it across.

". . . Mr. Twain has the habit of looking down sidewise into the middle of the desk on which he is leaning, while laughter in the audience continues. The bored and somewhat lugubrious expression he wears was slightly shaken by a twitching under his moustache."

Remember the open fly episode earlier in this prologue? You can see I was on the right track. It has worked on other occasions, too.

In Philadelphia he was reviewed in this manner:

"Mark Twain stumbled across the stage as if he had just been awakened from a sound sleep, groped around the reading desk in an aimless sort of way, and did not wake up until the entertainment was over. But in that dreamy, drawling fashion of his [he made them laugh]."

I've tried this, too. But where the percentage of television addicts in the audience is major, it does not work. *They* go to sleep. Television being what it is, this is merely a conditioned reflex. I suppose if we continue to watch television for five or six more years, without discarding it in disgust, the whole

* Cleveland *Leader*, December 18, 1884.
† New York *Sun*, November 19, 1884.

nation will be asleep. I make no predictions but I think it may be possible. I think television has done more to soften the backbone of America than any single thing, even Joe McCarthy. Sometimes, when I see one of those patients in the audience—always recognizable by the vacant stare, the folded arms, and the "you can't entertain me" attitude—I want to go down and shake him until his bones rattle. Whatever happened to the raw spirit of adventure in this country? Is it gone forever, or just asleep?

But to get back on the track again; I reasoned that while Twain's techniques must have been quaint in his day they would not be considered unusual in a humorist today. My problem was how to make Twain seem unconventional to a modern audience. What might be considered unusual in a lecturer today would be the smoking of a cigar during his performance. This would emphasize those qualities of casualness and uniqueness. So the cigar went in.

Secondly, the cigar served a purpose for me as an actor—a purely technical one. It gave me an activity on-stage. Puffing it, handling it, walking over to the ash tray to drop an ash, or maybe accidentally dropping one on the rug and rubbing it out with my foot, all these little devices helped me create an atmosphere of informality and, at the same time, gave me something to *do*. They also allowed me to slow down and think.

The most striking factor in the humorous style of Mark Twain is that he delivered his comic blockbusters with the innocent air of a man who does not realize he has said anything funny. He would ramble along and presently drop a remark which would set the audience off into gales of laughter, but he would take no notice of it. He might scratch his elbow, or stare off at some point in the auditorium which had suddenly become interesting to him; this would increase the comic effect of the remark. When the laughter subsided there would be a pause while Twain seemed preoccupied with some weighty matter; then another remark—again delivered without any visible awareness of its being funny; and while the audience was laughing at that, he might shuffle over to the reading desk and inspect his notes to make sure that he was sticking to his subject.

These are just a few of the techniques I have had to learn in an effort to stay alive on the stage for two hours. I have had to develop a whole repertoire of them, and in order to keep them fresh I must swap them around and invent new ones. If I am relaxed and open to suggestion during a performance, many little things will happen which offer opportunities for invention. A fly may come along and try to share the spotlight with me. The first time this happened I studied him awhile and presently he flew off and hid somewhere. A few minutes later I picked up the water glass and was about to drink from it when an idea came to me. I paused and peered into the glass. Then I looked at the audience. They tittered, which told me they had caught the idea. I set the glass down and said, "Well, if you think you can drink it, go ahead." Then I prayed the fly would stay out of sight.

I did not rehearse any of these devices in front of a mirror to calculate their effect. I rehearsed them on the audiences. In the beginning it was like going off the high board. I jumped—and then hoped I would hit the water pleasantly. If I didn't, it hurt. I am still jumping, and sometimes the impact is bruising.

My first performance of *Mark Twain Tonight!* was at the State Teachers College in Lockhaven, Pennsylvania, on March 19, 1954. I was terribly frightened about the whole thing. I drove out to Pennsylvania with a good friend, James Wells (Nancy's father), and he was my original stage manager, for that one performance. He saw the beginning of the whole thing. One of the warmest moments I experienced on my opening night in New York was when I looked out into the audience and saw Jimmy and his wife Agnes in the fourth row. This was during the third act, close to the end of the performance, and the look on their faces gave me a lump in my throat.

The performance in Lockhaven was a fifty-minute morning assembly. At that time the make-up was taking me only about an hour and fifteen minutes. (In the beginning, on the two-person show, I had done it in five minutes.) When I had it on and was ready to start, Jimmy wished me luck, someone introduced me to the student body, and I shuffled out. The applause an actor gets on his first appearance is always a wonderful help in a solo show, especially if it has any enthusiasm. It makes him feel that the people out front are glad they came, and glad to have you with them. That is the feeling I got in Lockhaven. My first line was, "I wish to begin this at the beginning lest I forget it altogether; that is to say, I wish to thank you for this lovely welcome you have given me." I remember figuring that the laugh or chuckles, if any, would come after the words, "lest I forget it altogether." But I got a pleasant surprise. A healthy burst of laughter broke into that first line right after the opening words: "I wish to begin this at the beginning." It lifted my heart from my shoes up to about my knees. The next laugh got it up a little higher, and as the laughs continued to come it kept rising and rising until pretty soon it was up where it belonged. I stopped gasping and began to breathe normally.

The show seemed to go along very well. The "Italian Guide" played better than I had hoped it would and by the end of half an hour I felt wonderful. The whole experience seemed so much easier than I had imagined it would be. I had not realized what a great writer I had working for me. Then I began what I felt would be a terribly funny selection: an episode I had carefully edited from "Captain Stormfield's Visit to Heaven." It concerns the efforts of an earthy old ship's captain from San Francisco to get past the pearly gates—the head clerk gives him an awful time because he can't locate San Francisco on the celestial map. When Captain Stormfield is finally passed in, they give him his wings and halo and harp, but he can't seem to manage them. When he tries out his wings he crash-lands every time. His halo won't stay on right, and the harp music gets on his nerves within half an hour. It all seemed terribly funny to me when I read it and I thought it was funny when I did it, but the audience's response fell off. It wasn't a disaster but it did diminish my confidence somewhat. They gave me a nice round of applause at the end of the show, yet I felt disappointed. Afterward, I asked one of the teachers why he felt the Stormfield number had not gone over better. He was reluctant to offer any criticism of it, but I pushed him. He finally said he thought perhaps the students had found it a little too irreverent.

This was to be the first of many lessons I would learn from Mark Twain—to wit: a story which will throw a human being into gales of laughter in private will very often draw his prim disapproval when told on the public platform. This is one of the little dishonesties of the race and it was to become one of the challenges I would have to cope with when doing Mark Twain. It is a good challenge. To make people laugh in public at things they are willing to laugh at in private makes them a little more honest. This is a purpose of humor: to make people honest. "Humor is the good-natured side of any truth," said Mark Twain.

At this point I was faced with the decision of having to

give up Mark Twain altogether. A few months before the
Lockhaven date I had finally landed a good job in television.
It was an important and continuing part in a TV and radio
daytime serial, *The Brighter Day*. I played a minister's son
and his name was Grayling Dennis. I looked up the name
"Grayling" in the dictionary and it said "an arctic bird." So
that was that. During the first nine months I became a reformed alcoholic, twice, and fell in love with a lady of ill
fame. It was an eventful life and in my opinion would strain
the capacity of an arctic bird as much as it strained mine.
Unless we have been underestimating the arctic bird.

The producers allowed me to fill most of the engagements
I had booked for that spring, but they did not want me to
book more engagements in the coming year which would
keep me off *The Brighter Day*. It was a good job with a
steady income, the first I had been able to achieve in some
time, and I needed it. I enjoyed it, too. Suddenly I was an
employed actor in New York City, and this meant a great
deal to me. But I am of a cautious nature and it has always
been my habit to look ahead and try to estimate what the
future will be like and what I can count on in the way of
security in this precarious business of theater. I had spent
six years doing a two-person show and it had been successful.
It was never hard to get bookings. Now I realized I had the
beginnings of a good solo show and that it was something
I would always be able to use in the future. So while I continued to do that soap opera, I also continued to work on
Mark Twain.

It is strange how events weave themselves together to
shape a career. By the end of nine months on *The Brighter
Day* I had become restless for something else. I was so restless, in fact, that when they gave me a ten-day vacation from

the show I got a wild impulse to go off somewhere by myself
and think everything out. I remember stopping on Fifty-
seventh Street one broiling September day and deciding that
what I wanted to do more than anything else was to go
skiing. I made inquiries. I found that I could go to Switzer-
land or Chile, but that the plane fare to these places was
formidable. An alternate choice was to fly out to the west
coast and ski on the glacier on Mount Shasta. I went that
afternoon to an air-line agency and bought a round-trip
ticket to San Francisco. Then I went home and told my wife.
I told her in the manner which she says I have always announced a brainless decision—firmly, shortly, and with a
definiteness which defeats the possibility of argument. I was
going up on Mount Shasta, alone, to go skiing and that was
that. What were we having for dinner?

I arrived in San Francisco with my skis and ski boots and
clothing for roughing it and made some inquiries about how
to get to Mount Shasta, and, once there, how to get up to
the glacier. I was told there was a one o'clock milk train out
of San Francisco for Shasta City. I thought: Fine, this will
add character to my adventure. In Shasta City I would be
able to find someone who would drive me up the mountain
as far as sixty-five hundred feet. From there I would have to
walk. The glacier began at ten thousand feet.

At the *hungry i* nite club in San Francisco I met a young
man who said he knew the mountain well and had often
climbed around on it and walked over other mountains in
the high Sierras with "Papa" Hemingway and his son, and
that he would be happy to lend me the very pack Hemingway's son had used. This was a marvelous stroke of fortune.
It drenched the entire adventure with a romance I could not
have dreamed of. And when he told me that Hemingway's
name was stenciled on the pack I could not wait to put it on

and start. It seemed to me, now, that I ought to climb to the very top of the mountain, if only as a gesture of respect to the name.

I said, "How high is this mountain?"

"Over fourteen thousand feet."

There seemed no end to my good fortune. I had never climbed anything more formidable than the subway stairs, but I had just lately finished reading *The Conquest of Everest* and the whole idea of climbing a mountain intrigued me. It seemed a lively adventure and one I could have a lot of fun describing to my friends back in New York. The fact that I had never climbed a mountain, knew very little about starting a fire, and was afraid of the dark when alone did not seem to make much impression on my mind.

I made quite a stir at the station with my pack and my skis and my rugged-looking outfit. I was wearing a pair of mountain-climbing boots for the full effect. The pack seemed heavier than I had expected. It was filled with equipment for camping which I had purchased in an army surplus store and it weighed in at sixty pounds. I tried to board the train with a graceful leap, but fell backward and had to try again.

On the train I met a sailor who had a bottle of cheap whiskey and we spent a riotous night diminishing that. I acquainted everyone with my plans. They were full of interest and wonder. As we toiled up through the magnificent valleys and sharp ridges of northern California, I kept a constant watch for my first sight of Shasta. I saw it at dawn, while in the diner having scrambled eggs. It came into view through a cleft between two high ridges, a stately pyramid of white, awesome in size, and higher than I had expected. I studied it thoughtfully, as one might study a bull in a pasture he wants to cross. My waiter came over, leaned across my shoulder, and pointed to it.

"There it is. That's Shasta. You sure you want to climb that?"

I said, "Yes."

"Man, you are in for some walk."

Then he told me all about the incident of the preceding year in which the guide conducting John Lindbergh's climbing party had fallen on the glacier, rolled down it, hit a rock, and been killed. I thanked him and he went away. The mountain seemed to be frowning at me, I thought.

When I got to Shasta City I went to the head forest ranger and asked directions of him on how to get up the mountain. He stood in Main Street and pointed out the route to me. I made no mention of the fact that I had never climbed a mountain before because I knew that he would disallow it if I did. I let him assume I knew all about it. This I achieved by keeping my mouth shut.

When the stores opened, I went in and bought some supplies: bacon, dried eggs, a couple of cans of beans, some frozen minute steaks, oleomargarine, and a long loaf of French bread. I reasoned the French bread would keep better than the other kind. I also bought several dozen bouillon cubes, and distributed them about my person so that if I got lost I could boil snow (I had a few Sterno cans) and have bouillon soup and thus survive. I bought lots of candy bars, too, for energy.

The weatherman agreed to drive me up to a place called Sand Flats at sixty-five hundred feet and from there I would have to walk the rest of the way. We arrived at Sand Flats—it is unnecessary to describe them—and he drove his station wagon slowly along a path in through the great redwood trees. It was uncomfortably dark in there. The sun was not able to penetrate them. He stopped in a little clearing and

I hauled out the pack—now over seventy pounds—the skis and myself, and propped everything against a tree.

He said, "I'll meet you here at four o'clock on Friday." That was four days hence.

"Okay."

"You sure you've got everything?"

"I think so."

"Well, I guess I'd better go. Don't forget—four o'clock."

"I won't forget."

"Well, good-by."

"Good-by."

He drove off. I watched his car back down the path until it was out of sight.

The first thing that occurred to me was that I was *all alone,* more alone than I had ever been in my life before. It was right then that I started looking for bears. I had made a good deal of inquiry concerning bears because I had had no experience with them and was naturally shy about meeting one. Everyone had assured me they were harmless; that if I saw one, all I had to do was pick up a rock and throw it at him. This did not seem reasonable to me and I had already decided that I would not do that if I saw a bear.

It was so still. The boles of those great trees were eight or nine feet thick and rose straight upward. Little sounds, all unfamiliar, came to me out of the forest. I stood there for a long time, contemplating what I had done, realizing that it was too late to turn back and wondering if I would ever see that weatherman again. I am ashamed to tell you the first thing I did. I went behind a tree and relieved myself. I don't know why it seemed necessary to go behind a tree to do it, but having just come from New York it seemed the natural way.

Then I put on my pack. It had never seemed quite so

heavy before and the straps cut into my shoulders as soon as I had it in place. I carefully hoisted the skis over one shoulder and started off. The trail was steep. It toiled upward through the forest along the edge of a ridge and I had to stop often and lean back against a tree to relieve the pain of the straps cutting across my shoulders. When I came to a stump I sat down on it, letting the pack take up most of the sitting room. I kept a constant watch for bears. I saw none but knew they were watching me and keeping out of sight until time for dinner.

I finally reached the Sierra Club hut at eight thousand feet, just above the timber line. The timber line is really a line. It is where the trees stop and desolation begins. Rising into the sky beyond the hut was the most formidable looking sight I had ever seen. Mount Shasta! I could not see the top of it. A sheer cliff of red stone cut like a waistband across the top of the glacial bowl and hid the peak from view. Above this band of red rock were two thousand feet of mountain I could not see.

I got my breath, deposited my trappings around inside the cabin, and had lunch. By this time I felt pretty good, so I studied the mountain and thought, "Well, I'll just climb up there to the glacier and take a few runs on the skis." I got a small knapsack out of the Hemingway pack and filled it with my ski boots, a few chocolate bars, and some bouillon cubes and started off. I had not gone a hundred feet before something very strange began to happen to me. My breath was coming in gasps. I could not seem to fill my lungs with air. It seemed to me that I must be sick. It never occurred to me until two days later, after I had gasped my way up to that glacier twice, that what was happening to me was what would happen to any damn fool who came from sea-

Photograph by Bernard Friedman

"If you can't make seventy by a comfortable road, don't go."

From thirty-five to seventy in three hours. *Photographs by Sy Friedman*

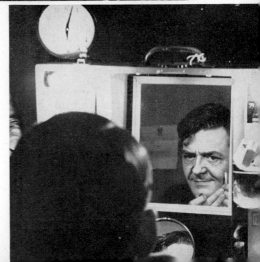

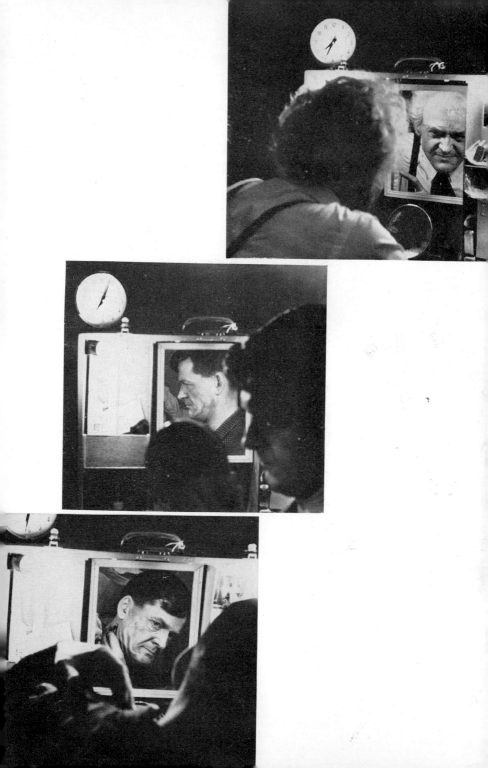

Photograph by Bernard Friedman

Hal Holbrook as Mark Twain

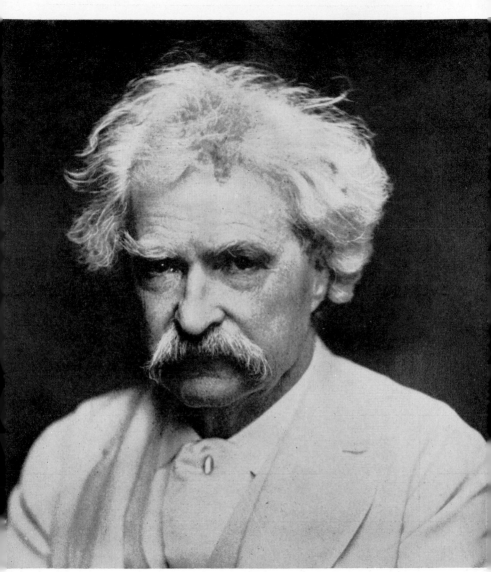

Photograph by Wide World Photos, Inc.

Mark Twain

Photograph by Bernard Friedman

"If I have seemed to love my memories of those days as a pilot on the Mississippi it is not so surprising; for I loved that profession far better than any I have followed since. . . ."

Photograph by Bernard Friedman

Huck: "We'd lay on our backs and smoke our pipes, looking away into the sky; not a cloud in it. . . ."

Photograph by Bernard Friedman

"A *man's* safe in the hands of ten thousand of your kind, so long as it's daylight, and you're not behind him!" (Colonel Sherburn in *Huckleberry Finn*)

Photograph by Bernard Friedman

"They said he could *vote* when he was at home! Well, that let me out!" (Huck's "Pap")

Photograph by Rolan Thompson

Hal and Ruby Holbrook as Rosalind
and Orlando (from *As You Like It*)

Photograph by Rolan Thompson

As Agnès and Arnolphe (from Mo-
lière's *The School for Wives*)

Mark Twain and the Interviewer (as originally done by Hal and Ruby
Holbrook; this is the first make-up Mr. Holbrook did for Twain). *Photograph by Rolan Thompson*

level New York to a point eight thousand feet up a mountain and tried to walk. It was the altitude.

That climb was the most cruel torture I had ever experienced in my life. I was stumbling along over a faint path marked by a line of large stones. The surface of the mountain was volcanic rock, shalelike in character, and every time I took a step forward, I slipped half a step back. It took me more than two hours to climb to the nine-and-a-half-thousand-foot level, and there I found a circular grouping of huge boulders which had settled themselves into a natural shelter. I saw that fires had been made in that shelter by previous climbers and the thought crossed my mind that if I could bring my sleeping bag up there and camp out in that spot one night, it would give me the early start I would need if I decided to climb the mountain. But as I stood there on the side of that barren place and ran my eye along the black crags rising to the right and left of me, crags with the razor-sharp backs of a dinosaur and looking for all the world as if witches ought to be dancing on them; and as I heard the mysterious sweep of the wind moaning past me, carrying along little wraiths of cloud, I decided that I would not camp out there after all. It is perhaps the only spot I have ever seen where they will never build a Dairy Queen.

The lip of the glacier was above me. It looked like such a short walk and such a gentle little hill, but I had already learned to be wary of what looked like gentle little hills and I decided against going up there that afternoon. I stowed my skis and ski boots in the shelter of one of the boulders, so that I would not have to lug them up again, and then stood up on top of a boulder and took a few pictures. I looked down, down the mountain to where the town was. I could barely see it. The clouds were scattered below me and all I could really identify the town by was the reflection of the sun on a tin roof. The terrifying thought crept into my mind that I would never get down there again. I cannot explain to you the feeling of isolation that came over me. The closest thing I can liken it to is what it must feel like to stand on the moon, alone.

I looked at my watch. It was four thirty. When I looked up again I saw a thin, ghostly line of foglike substance slipping toward me over one of those witches' crags. The thought suddenly smashed into my consciousness that I was not supposed to stay up there after four o'clock. This had been one point which the head forest ranger had been very careful to make. He had told me that if I stayed up there after that hour the clouds would close in and that I might get lost. Lost! I scrambled down off the boulder without pausing to say my prayers, checked my equipment, grabbed the knapsack, and started off. It seemed impossible to me that this foggy substance, which I supposed was clouds, could be closing in so quickly. I had never seen anything like it before. It was so silent and snaky, and it came so fast through the ridge. Before I had gone more than a hundred yards I found it impossible to see farther than fifteen or twenty feet in front of me. I stopped, no longer sure which direction to take. I was on a hump between two ravines, one to the left, one to the right. Since I could not see into the ravines, there was no way of identifying which was which and deciding upon the familiar one.

I thought, "I'm lost. It's Jack London all over again." Memories of London's stories came flooding back to me and I could see those poor fellows walking around and around in circles and always coming back to the same place and finally lying down to die. I said to myself, "Now, Holbrook, get charge of yourself; keep calm; just think it out carefully and start." I made my way slowly along the hump until I saw that I was walking over a field of pumice stone. This I remembered, and a great relief swept through me. The pumice stone field was something I had come across before. Blessed pumice stone. I was on the right route. I marched along with confidence now but wasting no time. The truth is, I didn't march along at all. I ran and fell along, always going downhill. Presently I came to a great boulder which had the numerals 88 painted on it in blue. I remembered having passed that and wondering what fool had come up there to paint 88 on a boulder and how he ever got the paint can up with him. As I stood there inspecting the boulder I heard a sound like the ripping of an old sheet. It came from the other side of the boulder. My first thought was "bear." There was a bear behind that boulder and I knew it. The question was, should I investigate or leave? It is strange how curious a man can be, even a frightened man, and I was not able to resist my nature. It seemed to me it would be better to *know* if a bear was there than to *not* know it and to wonder if he was following me downhill through the fog.

I crept cautiously around the boulder and looked. There was nothing there. My breath let go and I laughed at myself and turned to start off again. Suddenly the ripping sound came again. This time it did not stop. It became louder and louder and then I heard a rock whistle past my head. I suddenly realized what was happening. A landslide had started on one of those crags and I was in its path. I had been warned about landslides, especially on those crags where the rock was weathered and rotten. Now here was one being served up to me on the very first day. Was I to miss nothing in the way of romance? Another rock hit the ground and went singing off past me and I moved in close to the boulder for protection. By this time the explosions of sound had increased to a roar that was deafening. It seemed as if the whole mountain was coming down on top of me. I thought to myself, "Well, isn't this something? Everybody back home told me I was going to kill myself out here and now it's going to happen on the very first day." The humor of this struck me and I started to laugh. I threw my head back and laughed and laughed as one rock after another went whistling past. Presently the smashing and tearing and roaring began to diminish. I stood there for another thirty seconds or so and then everything was still. I had not been touched.

On the following day when I climbed up to this spot I saw that there had been a ravine between me and the crags, and that most of the avalanche had settled into that and this had saved me. But the incident, occurring as it did so soon, took away a good deal of my appetite for climbing that mountain, or any mountain so inclined to treat a stranger in such an inhospitable way.

I fell the rest of the way downhill without bothering to breathe or cope with other troublesome details until I reached the Sierra Club hut. By then darkness was falling. The timber line of spruce trees had turned from green to black. I looked inside the cabin to see if there were any large animals in there, then went inside and closed the door. But I couldn't keep it closed for long because I had to go outside and gather wood to start a fire. I gathered a quick armful of it, skipped into the cabin, and coaxed up a flame, trying to remember how Jack London's boys had built one, and then went out to get more wood to keep it going. Every time I came back with an armful of wood the fire had gone out and I had to rush out and get more. I finally settled for a low blaze, cooked up a minute steak and got out the French bread and the oleo, and had dinner.

There were no electric lights and I had forgotten to bring a candle. As the darkness gathered in closer, I hunted that

cabin over in a frenzy, looking for candles. I found two or
three short stubs and gratefully lit one of them, propping it
up on the wood table. When I had finished the meal I realized that I should have to go out in the dark and wash the
mess kit in a little stream about one hundred feet from the
cabin. I had bought one of those aluminum army mess kits
in the surplus store, and I knew that if I didn't clean it off
I would probably catch some kind of disease and die up
there all alone. I crept out into the darkness and headed toward that stream, looking to the right and to the left and
behind me and listening sharply and measuring the distance
back to the cabin all the time to make sure that I would have
a head start on a bear or any other four-legged animal that
came along.

I crouched down over the stream and scrubbed the mess
kit with sand to get the grease off, keeping one eye on the
black line of trees, where I sensed that all sizes of animals
were watching me with interest. Then I shot back for the
cabin, slammed the door, bolted it, and placed the heavy bar
across it. There were a few bright little embers still glowing
on the hearth. I watched them until they went out. Then I
crept into my sleeping bag and tried to go to sleep.

Curious sounds began to invade my consciousness and get
my imagination tuned up. I heard little feet running across
the beams overhead, and I knew what they probably were,
but decided not to investigate. I zipped the sleeping bag up
as high as it would go and made up my mind that if one of
those creatures dropped on my face I would try to be reasonable about it, but I would *not* allow one of them inside
the bag. I lay there for hours, listening. Then I dropped off
to sleep.

Presently I woke up again. It seemed to me that something
was prowling around outside the cabin, and its feet sounded

heavy. It would pause, then root around a little while, then pause again and make no sound, and then it would resume marching. I had to investigate. I couldn't stand the suspense. I got up and checked the door to make sure it was tightly closed and barred, then walked over to the little window and peered out. I could see nothing that looked like an animal, but rising above me in the moonlight was the bulk of Mount Shasta. It was the eeriest-looking sight I had ever seen.

I went to my knapsack and took from it a pint of whiskey which I had brought along for cuts and bruises. I took in two long draughts of it, put it down, went back to my sleeping bag, climbed inside, and that is the last thing I remember until eight in the morning.

It took me about two hours to make my breakfast and then I was ready to start climbing again. I was surprised to find that snow had fallen during the night. But the day was bright with a strong sun and the air was certainly the cleanest I had ever breathed. On the wall of the cabin was a large printed sheet with some history about Mount Shasta and the people who had climbed it. I was interested to find that, among others, a nine-year-old boy had got to the top. I began to dislike him immediately. It seemed to me that a nine-year-old boy had no right whatsoever to climb a mountain that was 14,162 feet high. I read further and found that this was not considered a hard mountain to climb. That anyone could do it. This is when I made the decision to climb it myself.

There was a topographical map on the wall also, and from it I was able to check the shape of the mountain against what I saw of it from the window, find my position, and follow on the map the route I should take—in a general fashion. I had had some experience with maps in the army and knew vaguely what all those little contour lines meant, and that the numbers under them referred to the altitude above sea level. The red cliff was at twelve thousand feet.

I started off in good spirits, but before long I was gasping for breath again. I still could not understand this. The fact would not penetrate my mind that I was a tenderfoot from the streets of New York and that the altitude was cutting down my wind. It was humiliating to me because I had been a distance runner in school and my long suit was endurance.

Some two hours later I crawled over the lip of the glacier on my hands and knees. I had got into this position on the way up that gentle slope just below it. I sat for a while, breathing deeply. It occurred to me that I ought to eat lunch. I was not hungry but I knew that I would have to keep up my strength. I decided on bouillon cubes. First it was necessary to melt the snow. But what I took to be snow turned out to be not snow at all; it was more like ice. I kicked at it with my boot until my toes hurt and still could not dislodge enough to get inside the pail of my mess kit. I gave up and used the water in my canteen. It took about a half hour for the Sterno to heat the water enough so that it could be used for soup, then I dropped in a bouillon cube and stirred it around until the water looked muddy and drank it. The mixture warmed my insides and that was pleasant, for there was a great wind cutting across the edge of the glacier. It was so cold I had to keep my mittens on and the hood of my parka tied tightly around my head. I wore dark glasses as a protection against sun blindness and spread white ointment on my nose to preserve that.

I looked up. About two thousand feet above me were those red cliffs. The slope leading to them seemed gentle most of the way and I could not see that there would be any difficulty in getting as far as the steep approaches below the cliff. I had been told that along to the right of them there was a rope which had been secured there by some former party and which would be useful in getting me up over the cliff. From that point, which I could not see in my position, it was a simple climb—just smooth ice with one dangerous crevasse which I would have to watch out for because if I didn't see it I would fall in. Locating the top of the mountain would be easy. I would know it when I came to it because it would be where I started going downhill on the other side.

I began walking across the basin of the glacier. It was like a small lake that had frozen over. It didn't seem to have any incline to it at all; it seemed to be flat, and yet I felt as if I was going uphill. It was remarkable to me how long it was taking to cross that little basin. It always looked as if there were only another few hundred yards to go before I should start up the steep slope at the foot of the cliffs. I kept putting one foot in front of the other, but my progress was discouragingly slow. I began to feel numb all over. It seemed to me that I had never been so tired in my life before. My thighs got heavier and heavier, and my knees seemed to have no control, as if there were air pockets in them which separated me from the rest of my legs. It was very still. Only the wind could be heard—the wind and my heart. I had never in my life heard it beat so clearly. I heard something crackle and stopped to look around. There was nothing—nothing but the white, hard snow and the sharp crags rising upward on either side. Then the crackling came again. It seemed to be *on* me. I reached up to my breast pocket and found a half-eaten Hershey bar. The loose paper around it had caused the loud crackling sound. I began to dwell upon the stories I had heard about abominable snowmen and I wondered if there could be any truth in them.

I stopped frequently now, stopped and tried to breathe deeply, but my lungs would not fill up with air. I began to count my steps: first twenty and then stop. Then fifteen. Soon I was down to ten between rest periods. I was across the lake now and starting uphill. My breath became more tortured and the air I took in was so cold it cut into my throat like fine sandpaper. It was necessary to be very careful, too, for the surface of the glacier was slick and I had been warned about falling. If one fell and did not have a pickax to stop oneself with, it would mean a long journey down and a crash landing against the cluster of jagged boulders at the foot of the glacier. Presently I was taking five steps and then stopping. My breathing terrified me, and the insistent and loud hammering of my heart seemed to be a warning. It beat into my ears and frightened me. Perspiration leaked down into my eyes and stung them. My body began to feel dismembered. There were legs and two arms and a head and something in between which housed a pounding heart, but none of these things were connected. I sat down to rest. It seemed to me that I could just sit there for ages. Between me and the ridge of red rocks was a wide, heart-shaped basin. At the lower junction of the heart was a huge boulder—it was this boulder which the Lindbergh guide had struck. I thought to myself that if I could just get up to that boulder I could sit there in its shelter, out of the path of the punishing wind, and decide what to do next. I began to crawl on my hands and knees. I crawled along for a count of five, stopped, and then crawled some more. Soon I began to fall down after every count of five, and remain that way awhile. I struggled up and began to count four, then three. I lost all track of time, all sense of counting; there was only the consciousness of rising to my hands and knees and groping a few feet forward and falling down again. My cheek pressed against the surface of the hard snow and it felt so cool and comfortable there. I would have liked to have stayed that way forever but it would not have been wise. I began to recall all the times in my life when I had been knocked down by one thing or another and had somehow got up and gone on again. This was the same routine, I thought; this was the pattern of life itself—"just one damned thing after another," as Mark Twain had put it. I braced myself on all fours and slowly drew myself up again, crawled another step forward, and fell flat.

I don't know how long I was asleep, but when I woke up I was lying flat with my face on the snow. I raised myself up and there was the boulder. At this point I gave up mountain climbing. I did not reach the top. I did not even have the pleasure of hoisting myself up over that cliff by the rope and avoiding the crevasse and standing on the top of the mountain.

I was beaten and I knew it. I would not try again. On the following day I went up to the glacier and did some careful skiing and for the first time I felt good; I could breathe more naturally. It was then I realized that I had become accustomed to the altitude. Occasionally I looked up toward the top of the mountain and thought to myself, "I could make it today. I feel better." But I did not have the heart to try. It was a raw day and there was snow in the wind and the upper reaches of the mountain were clothed in white mist.

Some day I would like to go back and try it again. I really would. But not alone; I would like to go in the company of somebody. It would mean so much to have someone along, to hear another human voice, not to feel the terrifying loneliness. Perhaps when my son is nine years old we will make a try at it.

A while back, before I got off the track, I started out to say how strange is the way events weave themselves together to construct a career. The restlessness which prompted me to try to climb that mountain now manifested itself in the attention I gave Mark Twain. I think I expected that up there on Shasta I was going to be able to solve a lot of questions which were bothering me. I think I expected that I would be able to commune with God, that if I could get up that high I would be in closer touch with him. It did not work out that way. I had been too frightened to commune with God or even myself. I don't ever remember laughing, except for that one time when the avalanche was coming toward me. Yet, oddly, when the weatherman picked me up on the fourth day and I began to tell him about my experience, I made fun of it. I laughed and treated it as a joke.

One thing he said to me, driving down the mountain, impressed me. I had finished telling him that this was my first experience in mountain climbing and he received this information in silence. Then I said, "You know, I feel like a coward. If I had been able to get to the top of that mountain, I think it would have been wonderful. But the mountain licked me—or maybe I licked myself—and I feel like a coward." He said, "You're no coward." Then he invited me home to dinner. We had trout fresh from a mountain stream. I met his wife and children, and they drove me to the train.

When I got back to New York I plunged into further study of Mark Twain and continued my work on the soap opera. Presently a friend of ours with the remarkable name of Lovey Powell, a singer who had been having a great deal of success in night clubs, suggested that I try out my Mark Twain impersonation as a night-club act. At first it seemed a ridiculous suggestion, but I thought it over and decided it would be an interesting experience. She got me an audition at a place called the Purple Onion, housed in a cellar beneath a bar on the corner of Fifty-first Street and Sixth Avenue in

New York. They put me on the bill. I stayed there for three weeks and "Mark Twain" as a night-club performer seemed to go pretty well. I worked up three fifteen-minute routines and varied them during the two or three shows I did every night.

The night-club life was new to me and exciting. I loved to listen to the trio—piano, bass and accordion—in the stretches between my show. It was a strange, romantic life which I had only read about or seen in the movies. There was something nostalgic about it, something lonely about the life of the people who worked there. Many strange types inhabit that world. The performers are nearly all individualists of a remarkable sort. They have to be. They battle their way night after night through some of the strangest experiences a performer can face. Each audience has a separate character of its own because the audience in a night club is small—just one or two people can turn it in any direction. I think it must be the most spontaneous kind of performing. The unexpected is always likely to happen, and you have to be prepared for it. You must learn to be sure of yourself, surer than you have to be on the stage where you are working with other actors who are going to do the same thing every night, and playing before an audience which knows its manners and minds them most of the time.

After a three weeks' run at the night club in February of 1955 I continued to work on the Twain material, looking for another chance to use it. Meanwhile, I decided that I wanted to learn to sing. I had in mind the idea that I would be a night-club singer. After taking lessons for nine weeks I decided, privately, that I was ready for my debut. I had heard about a talent night at the Lighthouse Café on Upper Broadway and decided that was where I would make my start.

The master of ceremonies was a confident man with oily

black hair and a loud tie and a habit of jumping up onto the tiny bandstand with a mock show of enthusiasm and slipping in a few worn jokes before urging forward the next trembling applicant. He gave me such a rousing introduction I knew I could not live up to it—so the game was up before I started. I climbed gingerly onto the bandstand, grasped the microphone for comfort, and did my first number, "I Got Rhythm." It was a deplorable failure. As I stared down at the row of faces around the bar and saw the disenchantment in their eyes, I knew that I did not have rhythm at all. After I had flatted my way through the interminable length of "I Got Rhythm," the master of ceremonies bounced onto the stand again, shoved me aside, spilled part of his drink on me, and said, "Ladies and Gentlemen, there you are. Hol Halbrook singing 'I Got Rhythm.' Now, Hol, what's your next number going to be?" I said, "Smile." He said, "Kid, you try to do that."

After my Lighthouse Café debut I made other forays at other talent contests and somehow managed to survive them without physical harm. Then one night I went down to the Champagne Gallery in the Village where anybody could sing who wanted to, and renewed my acquaintance with a young man named Brooks Morton who played a beautiful piano there. He urged me to get up and sing. With his encouragement I continued to go back there night after night, and before long I was able to get all the way through a song and still feel that life was worth living. Then Brooks Morton became Lovey Powell's accompanist.

Somebody—I think it was Lovey—came up with the idea of our opening a night club. She would sing, Brooks would play, and I would do Mark Twain. That's how a little place called Upstairs at the Duplex came into existence. It was down on Grove Street in the Village, off Sheridan Square, above the Duplex Bar and Grill. It was a fine little intimate room with charcoal gray walls and could seat about fifty people. We performed right on the floor in the curve of a small grand piano. The audience was never more than three feet away. Since we were managing the place ourselves, under the suspicious eye of the proprietor, we were able to lay down certain rules beneficial to the performance. One, no one would be admitted while an act was going on. Two, no drinks would be served while a performer was working. Once we got them in they had to stay. We did two or three shows a night, depending upon the extent of the crowd. Brooks played a set, followed by an intermission while drinks and food were served, then I came on for about fifteen minutes. Afterward there was another intermission, and then Lovey did her act. This continuous routine was repeated three times a night with the late show starting around one thirty in the morning. I played there for seven months and it was altogether the most valuable performing experience I have ever had, particularly for the development of Mark Twain's style of delivery.

There was no hurry. People who came there came to see our show. Occasionally, it is true, a tourist lost in the back streets of the Village would venture in and wonder where the chorus girls were. When I appeared in white suit and wig it generally gave them a fright. There were no introductions to the separate acts—we simply appeared from a door at the rear of the room—so you can imagine how important it was for me to identify myself as "Mark Twain" as quickly as possible. If I did not, there was sure to be comment. On one occasion a lady, out for a night on the town, broke the hush with, "My God, it's Colonel Weatherbee." Another time I heard a male voice saying, "Marion, what kind of a place is this?"

The man who wrote the column listings for the *New Yorker*, "Pops" Whitaker, got behind us at the start and helped spread the news. A sophisticated and interesting crowd of people began to migrate down to the Village to see us.

Right from the start we had trouble with the ladies' room door. It happened that this door was placed squarely behind the area in which we performed, so that if it became urgently necessary for a lady to use those facilities she had to cross directly in front of us, forcing us back into the curve of the piano, walk around to the rear of us, open the door, and go in. This feature did not really do much toward helping along the illusion that I was Mark Twain. Often, as I paused before delivering a favorite punch line, the door would open and out would come a lady to share the spotlight with me. I found this competition unnerving and insisted that the door be relocated. We accomplished this job on an off night, working around the clock. Since we were short of money, we had to take the door and frame apart very carefully and then reassemble it in the place we had made for it out in the back hall. We filled in the hole left in the wall behind the acting area, working furiously, and got it painted just as the first guests began to arrive.

The new position for the ladies' room door out in the back hallway improved the quality of our performance, but it presented problems while we were waiting to go on. We waited in the back hall. Very often a lady would leave her table, open the door into the hallway, and walk smack into Mark Twain. She would back up and eye me curiously, and then pass into the ladies' room. While in there she would have time to settle her mind. When she came out she was ready for me.

"Say, who are you anyway?"

"Mark Twain."

"So I'm Betsy Ross. Now tell me another."

It was worse when a lady came through packing several drinks in her. She would barge into the hallway under a full head of steam, pull up short, look me over and say, "You're cute," then lurch into the ladies' room. I always hoped I would not get on before she came out because then I would have to lock the door into the club to keep her from passing through my act. Then there was almost always an explosion when she exited from the ladies' room and found she'd been locked out in the hall. She would rattle the door awhile, demanding to be let in, and those people seated at the tables near by would begin to look uneasy and lose interest in my performance. The door rattling might continue for several minutes, while the outcast pleaded and then demanded to be let in. Once she realized that Mark Twain was not going to oblige she began to air her views, much to the enjoyment of the audience at that end of the room. Some of those ladies became quite violent and abusive before retiring down the back stairs leading to the kitchen and bar and asking directions about getting back into the club. Others, with more endurance, raged at me until my act ended and I unlocked the door. Then there was hell to pay. They lectured me for five or ten minutes before I was able to escape to the dressing room.

The alternative to this was leaving the door unlocked. If I did that I ran the risk of having her weave into the spotlight on her return trip and engage me in conversation in front of the audience. Since I was trying to maintain the illusion that I was Mark Twain, this was sure to be demoralizing. I had lost control of the audience on more than one occasion when a wild-eyed lady, fresh from the back hall, stopped to interview me about the books I had written or tell me of her visit to Hannibal.

One of the stories I used to tell in the club is the one about the man who contracts to carry a deceased friend back to Wisconsin to be buried. At the railway station the coffin box is mixed up with a box of rifles, so that when the man climbs into the box car to accompany his dead friend on that last journey, he is keeping company with a box of rifles. Just as the train is ready to leave a fellow jumps into the car with a small package of limburger cheese and places it on one end of the supposed coffin. It being a wintry night, the old box-car attendant bolts the doors and window against the cold and works up a fire in the stove. Before long the odor begins to work up, too, and the suffering those two men go through on that long night ride, and their desperate attempts to "modify" the corpse is told in a hilarious way by Mark Twain. The selection is included in this volume, in Act One.

One night at the club I began this story just after the couple at the table in front of me had been served two large steaks. I did not notice this until I was well into the story and immediately I began to feel sorry I had chosen it. They were going after those steaks with relish, carving off choice pieces and plunging them into their mouths, and then they began to slack up. As I described the odor in the box car, the forks paused awhile in mid-air before completing their journey. The chewing became more meditative and the expressions on their faces hung somewhere between suspicion and loss of hope. I went relentlessly on, describing the probable length of time the deceased had been gone and the frequent trips to the window for fresh air on the part of the two trapped men in the box car, and all the while I was casting desperately about in my mind for some quick way to end the story and leave those poor people with whatever remaining pleasure they could find in the steaks. But there seemed to be no way out. I saw one of the forks rise, pause, then retreat to the plate. A carving knife was laid down. The two faces were gazing at me now with a mute appeal which wrung my heart, but I could do nothing. Presently the two plates were pushed quietly away and the stricken diners eased back in their chairs, dumbly waiting for the completion of that dreadful tale. It came at last, and when I left them they appeared to be leaning against each other for support, hands folded, eyes glazed, steaks cold. I never told the story again.

During the seven months I worked in that night club I was able to develop two and a half hours of material. This was the foundation of my repertoire of Mark Twain. It was an exhausting schedule, for I had two radio shows in the morning and a television show in the afternoon two or three times a week. I arrived at the club about eight thirty in the evening, made up for two hours, and did two or three shows, depending on the extent of the crowds. As a rule I did not get home until three or four in the morning, sometimes later when there were managerial problems to thrash out. We had plenty of them. I often worked until dawn on new material, rehearsing it in my head while riding the subway. The research took hours and hours and sometimes it required a week to locate and put together just two or three minutes of new material. I was tired all the time, but I hung on in the hope that someday the long hours would pay off. My salary at the club, after paying my share of the press agent's fee and the advertising, came to about forty-five dollars a week.

But there were many compensations not measurable by money. I was learning to hold an audience under the most challenging circumstances. I was learning how to use the pause for maximum effect, how to take my time, and how to

relax under conditions of pressure. These would all serve
me someday. And I was learning from Brooks and Lovey
how an artist must develop unshakeable confidence in himself and his own work. They are both wonderful performers
and their teamwork was rare and sensitive and a joy to behold. Lovey in particular seemed to have a belief in herself
which was sometimes nearly savage in its intensity. I have
seen her go in front of an unruly audience and take command of them by the sheer force of her belief in what she
was doing. She is an actress who sings, not merely a vocalist.
There is point and purpose in her interpretation of a song
and she delivers it with a conviction which mesmerizes an
audience. It was from her that I learned the importance of
conviction in the delivery of my material. The audience may
like or dislike you but, if the conviction is there, they listen.

One night Ed Sullivan came to the club. It was the early
show and he was seated at the table directly in front of our
playing area. I chose what I felt was my funniest material
(the accident insurance routine got the biggest laughs at
that time) and went out and did the show. There were just
two couples in the room, besides Sullivan.

When I had finished he called me to his table and asked
me to be on his TV show. I was thrilled. It was the break I
had been waiting for. Although my appearance on the Sullivan show was brief and hardly memorable, it did open certain doors to me. Steve Allen asked me to do his *Tonight*
show. Fees for my concert engagements increased and more
of them became available. I received requests to appear at
Angel's Camp, California, for the Calaveras County Fair and
Jumping Frog Jubilee, and to play Mark Twain in Hannibal,
Missouri. Another development of great value to me was a
performance at Hartford, sponsored by the Mark Twain
Memorial. I met people there who became my friends and

supporters and I have the greatest admiration for the remarkable job of restoration they have been doing on Twain's unique home in Hartford. There I met Miss Katharine Day, a descendant of Harriet Beecher Stowe, and the present occupant of the Stowe house which is adjacent to Twain's. She had played with the Clemens children as a child and her memories of Samuel Clemens gave me some insight into the gracious side of his character.

I was slowly becoming identified with Mark Twain, but this presented a certain danger. As a result of the Sullivan show, news of what I was doing spread as far as Hollywood. I knew this because I was contacted about playing the role of Gramps in a planned television series of *You Can't Take It with You.* When I went to the New York office of the film company for my interview the casting director there thought those people out in Hollywood had played a joke on him. He did not expect to see a thirty-one-year-old actor come through the door, and it gave him somewhat of a turn. I spent a good deal of time establishing the fact that I was the actor who had done the Mark Twain bit on Sullivan's show and then he said he would send me a script. That was the last I heard about *You Can't Take It with You.*

The danger was this: *I* wanted to be the one to get Mark Twain to Broadway, but I knew that if an established star came up with the same idea he would get there before me. So now it became a race against time. I made a decision. I was working daytimes on radio and *The Brighter Day* TV serial, and I was working nighttimes in the night club. I was also continuing my singing lessons and doing rather well with them. I had auditioned for several Broadway musicals without any notable success, but I was developing a voice. I was also developing into a very tired man. I remember sitting down one day and thinking the matter over. It seemed to me that I was splitting myself up into three parts, and that if I really hoped to succeed in any of these three endeavors I should have to give up at least one of them. *The Brighter Day* was no great problem because it had become routine to me now and I only appeared on it about twice a week, so it became a choice between the singing career and Mark Twain. I chose Mark Twain. I was sorry to give up the singing lessons because I enjoyed them tremendously and perhaps some day I can go back to them again.

I then made an arrangement with the producers of *The Brighter Day* which would allow me to get off the show for several weeks during the fall and several more during the winter and spring, during which time I could go out on tour and play a total of forty or fifty engagements a year with Mark Twain.

I now began working for length, pushing the time of the show beyond the one-hour-and-a-half limit which I had established. I was using one intermission. I found that the show worked best when I ran for about fifty minutes, then took a fifteen-minute intermission, and then added another thirty or forty minutes. The real key to holding audience interest as long as that when you are alone on the stage is variety. You must always be shifting the ground beneath their feet, always catching them off guard, always making them wonder what is going to happen next. There must be little changes of mood and certain big ones. The overall mood of the show is comedy, but it starts out with one kind of comedy and matures into a deeper kind. For the first half hour, I simply work on the audience to make them laugh. I try to give them confidence in the slow, casual, easy-going delivery and personality of Mark Twain, to make them realize that nobody has to be in a big hurry in order to create laughter. This is an important point in the show because so many of our audiences today are used to the rapid-fire delivery of comedians and having the punch lines delivered to them with the impact of atomic explosions. This is not the way with Mark Twain. He meanders around and creeps up on you when you are not noticing. He places his little bomb in an unprotected place and then quietly walks away while it explodes. The audience has to learn to expect these explosions, to recognize when they are coming, and to begin to savor them. The humor at first is very broad, then it begins to develop a point of view, satire creeps in around the fringes, and the audience must be made to realize that beneath the veneer of humor a deadly commentary is often being made.

In the two-act format I end the first act with the dramatic account of the Boggs-Sherburn shooting and the attempted lynching. This begins mildly and harmlessly enough with little explosions of mirth here and there and then slowly gathers up into a savage blockbuster aimed at the cowardice of man. In the second half of the show I begin with a satiric selection which will also provide a good deal of laughter, such as the "Advice to Youth," and then tell the "Ghost Story" for a change of mood. By the end of the "Ghost Story" the time has come for some reminiscences about his boyhood, which are both funny and pathetic, and then, perhaps, the touching story of how he got the name Mark Twain. The show ends usually with his advice on how to get to be seventy.

The show has to be constructed in such a way that as the evening progresses the audience comes closer and closer to Mark Twain. To begin with, we are dealing with a character who did not wear his heart on his sleeve. He was a man. His attitude is that if you don't wish to stay and hear him, you are at liberty to go home. There is no coercion. It won't really matter. He'll just stay up there and talk as long as there is anyone left to listen. During the first half or two-thirds of the show he is conducting a lecture; he is playing for an audience; he knows it and the audience knows it. But as the evening progresses and the audience becomes aware that there is more to this man than meets the eye, that there is more than just laughter in him—that in some cases there is profound truth behind the humor he delivers so casually—they become involved in figuring him out; at least, I hope they do. After the "Ghost Story" the feeling of a lecture is gone, and from then on you might be sitting in the parlor with him, listening to some of the intimate things which a grand old man is carrying in his heart.

The three-act version of the show is an extension of this format. The first act runs thirty-five or forty minutes and its aim is to generate as much laughter as possible and to leave the audience at the first intermission with the feeling that Mark Twain in person is a good deal funnier than they had expected. The second act starts off with more humor, to reassure those skeptical ones that he can still make them laugh when necessary; and then comes the biggest mood change in the show, with the introduction of the *Huckleberry Finn* number. This selection is, to my mind, the most important one in the evening. It has in it the message of brotherhood and human dignity which I feel is needed today. After *Huckleberry Finn* I try to give the audience the so-called pessimistic side of Mark Twain. Here we deal with a humorist's commentary about the human race, but the humor now is savage and pointed and, for those who are prepared to take it, it can be something of a revelation. The second act ends with this presentation of the case of Mark Twain versus Man.

The third act begins with the "Ghost Story" and achieves two things, I think. It changes the mood completely again, while at the same time gripping the attention of the audience. Once it is over the time has come to take the rest of Mark Twain apart. He and the audience are well acquainted now. They have shared what I hope is an evening of laughter and a few tears. An understanding has been established between them. It is now possible for the man Mark Twain to speak more gently about the personal things he carries around in his heart.

There is one more shift of mood. It comes with the shrugging off of nostalgia and the return to the positive humor of the seventy-year-old advice. By the end of the show it is my hope that everyone in the audience can feel that they might have been seeing Mark Twain. If I can leave them with that conviction, then I have done my job.

In June of 1957 I arrived at another important stop on the road to Broadway. I had written Jean and Carlton Guild, who run the summer playhouse in Holyoke, Massachusetts. I had worked for them for three seasons some years before and I knew they had a good deal of faith in me. I asked them if they would consider opening their season of summer stock with my solo show, *Mark Twain Tonight!* In a few days I got a letter back from Carlton and it began in this way: "Dear Hal: The light is green. . . ."

This was a very important break for me because, if successful, I would have established the fact that I had a three-act evening in the theater, not just a lecture. I knew that the audiences up in Holyoke and Springfield, Massachusetts, would be friendly to this venture, and so did Jean and Carlton. The reception was very heartening indeed. Critically it was wonderful. The audience turnout was not overwhelming, but considering the fact that it was the opening week, it was not bad. Also, I was playing in a huge casino seating one thousand, all on the same floor, and for one person to hold an audience under those conditions was a considerable challenge. The success I felt there in Holyoke convinced me that I was ready to make a try for Broadway.

Back in the night club, another link in this chain of events had been formed. I had joined The Lambs, the actors' club in New York, and I met there an intense young man named Jerry Guardino. He was presenting a play in the beautiful theater on the third floor of the club, but it was a short play and he needed something else to round out the evening. He heard about my Mark Twain night-club act and came down to the club to see me. Then he asked me to do a thirty-five-minute performance in conjunction with the production he was presenting at the club. It met with a great deal of success and struck the fancy of certain people who saw it. One of these persons was John Lotas. About two and a half years later John was the man who brought me to Broadway.

During the fall, after my Holyoke engagement, Jerry Guardino introduced me to John Lotas, and we began to plan for an off-Broadway production of *Mark Twain Tonight!* First we organized a "backers'" audition to be held at the Astor Hotel in a small banquet room. We had no experience in "backers'" auditions but we secured at this time the services of a press agent, Maxine Keith, who was wise in the ways of the theater and gave freely the counsel and help we needed. Her faith in the project was a wonderful thing and I shall not forget it.

None of us could get hold of a very promising list of investors but we scraped through our memories and rounded up forty-five people, some of whom we felt might have money to risk in our project. On the night of the audition it began to rain. It rained very, very hard. It rained us out of "backers." We had a few people there from whom we drew pledges amounting to several thousand dollars, but it was not enough. We needed nine thousand. We withdrew from this first skirmish, bound up our wounds, and planned a further campaign.

John and Jerry got permission to put on a performance at the Lambs Club—that is, if we could secure a charitable organization to buy out the house. It seemed to me a formidable task to find any organization willing to pay twenty-five dollars a seat and guarantee two hundred and sixty candidates, but I did not then realize the energy and determination contained within the persons of Messrs. Lotas and Guardino. They got one. It was the Ophthalmological Foundation, an organization of people dedicated to the blind. Since Mark Twain had been one of the original founders of the Lighthouse and the moving factor in raising the money for Helen Keller's education, this was a happy reunion.

The performance took place in January of 1958 and it was one of the most exciting I have ever had. The response was thrilling, especially when I realized that I was playing before a group of theater-wise people, people who had come in full dress, people who on other occasions had chosen Broadway productions for their theater parties. I heard some bravos and shouts of "More!" at the end of the performance —I was listening very closely—and when I realized that I had been performing for two and a half hours, I was convinced that I could make a success of the show in a Broadway theater.

Following this happy occasion, the Lambs Club allowed us to give a performance free to its membership. This was scheduled for a month later, in February. We launched into furious activity. We approached every available investor we could locate and urged him to attend the forthcoming performance. We approached several hundred. Forty-four

pledged that they would attend. The performance was scheduled for the seventeenth of February, my birthday. I did
an engagement on the fourteenth at the Music Hall in
Houston, which was a gratifying success, and started homeward on the plane with spirits high. When we got to Bir-
mingham, Alabama, I saw with some disbelief that there was
snow on the ground. In Atlanta planes were grounded and
I spent the night in a hotel. I managed to get a flight going
north to New York in the morning and we landed in Newark
in the midst of the worst blizzard to hit New York in quite
a few years. There was so much snow on the runway that a
path had to be laboriously shoveled through it for the stairs
to be put up against the plane. When I arrived in Manhat-
tan there were no taxis running. The streets had not even
been cleared off. Drifts were piled everywhere and very few
cars ventured out. It was a hopeless snarl in the city.

The following night, after another healthy snow, we gave
the performance at the Lambs Club. Of the forty-four
backers we had expected, three showed up. Admiral Byrd
was not one of them, but they were of that breed. We held
no more "backers'" auditions that year.

Jerry Guardino, who had toiled hours and hours in my
behalf during that long season, went to California to seek
employment there. He had just been married and it was no
longer possible for him to live on no income and work hard
for it.

That summer John and I formed a partnership under the
name of Mark Productions Company. Our long-range plan
was to get the show into a theater. Our short-range plan was
to have an office downtown where we could amuse ourselves by pretending to be busy. We rented an office in a
run-down, characterful building on West Forty-fourth Street
just off Times Square. It was a one-room affair on the third

floor and had two windows looking out on the street. If you leaned very far out you could see Sardi's on the other side of the square. In the building across the street, on the second floor, ample diversion was provided by an Afro-American Dance Class, which rehearsed to the beat of bongo drums; on the floor above there was a lady who provided diversion of a different sort. We placed our two desks in front of these windows and watched the passing parade. Often we worked. At other times we just sat there with our feet on the desks, like producers, and planned the big things we were going to do. John, who is really a very active radio announcer and narrator, was busy on the phone most of the time, and I kept occupied writing letters and working on new Mark Twain material.

I had a phone, too. John's phone had a row of four or five buttons on it, only two of them live. One was his line, one was mine. As a conservation measure my phone had but one button which you turned to the right or to the left to get on or off of one or the other of the two lines—I was never able to find out which. I could not understand this system at all. It frightened me. If I was alone in the office, engaged in conversation on my phone, and the other one rang, I was thrown into confusion. It seemed that no matter which way I turned my button I would lose somebody and if I tried pushing John's buttons I would lose both of them. I called the telephone company and had them explain the system to me but was not successful in carrying out their instructions. I still lost one or the other party.

One day as John and I were seated at our desks a curious thing happened. Both phones rang simultaneously! At first it seemed to us that only one phone had rung. We waited and when they rang again it was apparent that both phones were ringing together. We smiled at each other and picked up the receivers. The party on my phone wanted John; the party on his phone wanted me. We looked at each other. It was a terrible decision—which button do you push in a spot like that? We solved this problem by getting up and exchanging phones. The system worked. It seemed to us that we had made an improvement over the system recommended by the telephone company, so we called them and tried to explain it to them. They could not understand it. Thus, another advance was lost to them.

In May of last year, 1958, I appeared as Mark Twain on the *Wide, Wide World* television program devoted to "the sound of laughter." As a result of this John and I were approached by Coronet Films to do a short educational film about Mark Twain. In the fall of last year, we worked continuously on the script for this film, while also fulfilling our other engagements, and by February we were ready and organized to go ahead with the film. At this time a friend of John's, Bunker Jenkins, approached him with a proposition for another "backers'" audition. I gave it in his apartment, in the living room. There were six people present. I did not do the whole show, only about one hour and a half of it. At the intermission one man asked for a pen and wrote out a check for four and a half thousand dollars. That was the start we needed. After that, the rest of the money came swiftly.

Meanwhile, I had a tour scheduled in the far Midwest for March. We planned to open as soon as I returned to New York. When I left on the tour the money had not yet been fully raised and I was still not certain that we would open. As I went about from Texas to Iowa in a state of suspense, I looked for telegrams. Finally one came. It said we were in. The money was raised; we would open April 6 at the Forty-first Street Theater. It was then that I began to get nervous.

One cannot appreciate the terror of an opening night in New York unless he has experienced it. I had never experienced it before and in this case I would have no company on the stage with me to share the traditional fright. But John was confident and very reassuring. While I was away he carefully and calmly organized the whole thing. He hired a wonderful press agent, Harvey Sabinson, who had worked for Borge during his very successful run, and this I felt was a great plum for us. Bunker Jenkins was to be co-producer and he bent his energies to the preparations for the opening. When I arrived back in New York there was about a week left before opening night. My wife was calm, John was calm, everybody was calm except me. I wasn't so calm. It seemed to me there was a great deal to do yet. There was, for instance, the furniture to locate. It consisted of merely a chair, a table, and an old-fashioned lectern, but these are formidable objects when you don't know where to look for them. They had to be of the right period, height, and character. The procuring of these articles had been left for me, since it was felt that I would know what to look for.

I found the chair and the marble-topped table at the Salvation Army and also bought a short dictionary stand there. At an antique shop on Greenwich Avenue in the Village I saw an ornate hatstand, a beautiful mahogany piece. I bought it and gingerly cut a three-foot section out of the post, then dismantled the dictionary stand and had the post joined to its feet and table top. The result was an authentic old reading stand with a very slight list to port which gave it a further hint of character. On the afternoon of the opening night I went down to the Village again and found a cut-glass pitcher, an old tumbler, and an old-fashioned ash tray which had a receptacle for wooden matches. Then I went to the theater and started my make-up. By this time it had become a three-hour-and-fifteen-minute job.

Telegrams began to come in. So many more than I had ever dreamed would arrive. They came from all parts of the country, from friends, from people who had engaged me to appear in their schools, from relatives and old classmates. About half an hour before curtain time I stopped and began to read some of them. I don't know how many I read, but I began to get a terrific lump in my throat, and I cried. It had not occurred to me that so many people would take the trouble to wish me good luck.

When eight forty came I went backstage and tried to tell myself that this was just another performance in Wahoo, Nebraska. I had been disappointed time and time again and I braced myself for another blow. I told myself that no matter what the critics said, I knew I had a good show and a worthy one, and that it wouldn't really matter. But this was mainly bluff. It did matter. It mattered because twelve years of my own energy and thought had prepared me for this performance. It mattered because four years of physical and mental strain had been donated by my wife during the years we had spent on the road playing all those tiny towns. It mattered because people like Ed Wright and Bim Pond and Ricklie Boasberg (the lecture manager who delivered us from school assemblies) and Lovey Powell and John Lotas and many others had encouraged me and expected me to do well. None of those critics on the other side of the curtain had ever heard of me before. But I had heard of them.

The overture music began. The jaunty sound of the banjo propped me up and when the curtain opened it propelled me onto the stage. I stood there through the applause which greeted the make-up, and then it suddenly struck me with

tremendous force just what I was doing—that after all this
time I was really standing on a stage all alone in front of
those Broadway critics—and I don't believe I have ever been
so frightened by anything in my life. For more than two of
the three acts I felt exactly as I had on that mountain. I
could not seem to stay up. I kept feeling that I was falling.
The response came but it did not come easily, it did not roll
in smoothly, it was not the rhythmical kind of response an
actor can lean on and play with and enjoy.

At the end of the first act my wife came backstage, smiling
confidently, and said, "Where's the fire? Slow down." That
helped me. I knew I was rushing it. At the end of the second
act I was still not convinced that I had won over the audience. My knees were visibly shaking. John came back and
assured me that I was doing a fine job and that everybody
was loving it. This I could hardly believe. Toward the middle
of the third act after I told the story about how Mark Twain
got his name, I felt for the first time that I was in control.
I knew I could go the rest of the way. I sat on the edge
of the table and delivered the seventy-year-old material with
pleasure and relish, and I took my time. I looked out into
the audience and identified certain people—my wife, Jimmy
and Agnes Wells, Bim Pond and Agnes McTernan, and my
aunt and uncle from Cleveland. I saw victory in their faces.

An actor's memory may be likened to a well. From it he
draws up the experiences that have come to him along
through life, and he uses these in translating the experiences
in the life of the character he plays. If the well of memories
lies deep, the actor will draw from it a life for his character
that is fresh and personal and true. One of the reasons actors
become actors is that these memories rise up in them. They

will not stay down. They overflow. And so the actor finds expression for them on a stage.

Occasionally a happy thing happens. An actor finds a role in which the memories of his own experiences rush out to join those of the character he is creating. It is much the same as if you made the acquaintance of someone at a party and found that you shared common interests, experiences, convictions—and you talked all night. My relationship with Mark Twain has been something like that. I find in him reflections of myself. I say "reflections"; I do not mean that I am "just like him." I am not, nor do I want to be. When the actor who plays Lincoln begins to think he is Lincoln, he is dead. But I do have, I think, something in common with Mark Twain, just as have many other people who have read and loved his books. When I read Mark Twain my actor's well begins to stir and bucketfuls of memories come hand-over-hand from it. His humor refreshes me; his whimsy, his nonsense, his savagery and heartache uplift me and give me a cleansing catharsis, mentally and emotionally. There is in Mark Twain that quality of earthbound compassion and a mischievous style of communicating it that always leave me with a forgiving attitude toward the human race, myself included, no matter what idiocies I have just finished reading about in the newspaper or committed myself.

Twelve years of research have gone into *Mark Twain Tonight!* and it has been fun. The quality of the research has not been pedantic. I have sought for the man, not only in his books and in the places where he lived, but in myself as well. When I visited Angel's Camp, California, I had myself driven over four or five steep hills to the ancient cabin on Jackass Hill where Twain wrote his first version of the Jumping Frog story. The sight of the cabin filled me with wonder—wonder that our great writer had been "born" here, that a simple story he heard in a tavern at Angel's could have launched such a meaningful career. I stood in front of the rough stone fireplace and noticed that no mortar joined the stones. They had been shaped together laboriously by men who had no resources but their own ingenuity. It is true that Twain may have "sat and watched while his companions did the work," but he was there, nonetheless.

I realized, too, that in front of this fireplace he had learned the art of storytelling. It was here with Steve and Jim Gillis that he had spent a long winter, and a major diversion had been the retelling of tales grown old with use, and so it was necessary to improvise, to embellish and enlarge them as the storyteller went along. I could hear in that cabin the echo of long lost chuckles and the drawling cadences of Jim "Baker's" bluejay yarn. Somewhere I had read that Twain found himself as a writer after he went on the platform, that from that time on he wrote as he talked. One can find proof of this in the written versions of his speeches. There is little difference between the style and wording in them and in passages in his books. So here is where the literary style of Mark Twain began—on this hearth in a weathered cabin in the remote mountains of northern California. Perhaps this explains the intimacy and directness of his writing.

I made a trip to Hannibal in the summer of 1957 to appear as Mark Twain. The people there are reserved, even shy, and there is polite caution in the manner in which they accept you. I thought of Mark Twain's words, "I came from an undemonstrative race." The frontier character is distinguishable in Hannibal today, as it is in most of the small towns between the Mississippi and the High Sierras. A man is not eagerly taken in as a friend. He must prove himself a little. No judgment is passed until he does that.

There is a man out there who has been kind to me. He

is John Winkler, proprietor of the Becky Thatcher Book Shop and a moving force in keeping alive the spirit of Mark Twain in Hannibal. One day he drove me to the top of "Lover's Leap" south of town, which commands a view of the town and the river. It is peaceful up there, and the lazy sounds of Twain's boyhood sing their measured cadences in the sun. Insects chatter in the heat. The town drowses in the valley below and beside it the sinuous tide of "the great Mississippi, the majestic, magnificent Mississippi" rolls endlessly along. It was here that I found the pulse beat for Huckleberry Finn. I think of that moment when I pause in the show to settle into the boy's character.

In Act Three where Twain describes his boyhood on his uncle's farm, I can call up deep memories of my own. The happiest days of my life were spent on a farm in South Woodstock, Connecticut. I doubt if I realized at the time that they were going to be the happiest days, but as I look back on it now I realize they were. It was a chicken farm run by Uncle Sabe and Aunt Ruby Spalding. They weren't really my aunt and uncle, but I called them that just the same. They had an old farmhouse about two hundred years old, and acres and acres of land, much of it taken up with chickens and corn. There was a brook running around two sides of the property, a fine clear stream that had a deep bend at one point where the annual floods had torn away a good portion of the bottom and created a magnificent natural swimming pool fifteen feet deep in one place. There was a homemade diving board and a high bank around one side of the bend that was lovely for taking a long run and jumping over. The water was cold and refreshing, and there was a shallow place with a gravelly bottom where you could sit and run your fingers through the pebbles. There was a dilapidated rowboat, ideal for turning upside-down so that it rested gently on its gunwales and allowed you to dive underneath and stick your head up in the air space and make wild, Indian sounds, and feel very mysterious. There were woods and fields all around. There was a porch that took in two sides of the farmhouse, with rocking chairs, where you could sit at dusk of the evening with Uncle Sabe in his rocker, one arm hooked over the back, and listen to him talk and wave at friends who went by on the state road.

There were magnificent meals, great feasts around a dining table so burdened with food that it leaned a little to one side in deference to the toil it was put to. We ate family style. Besides Aunt Ruby and Uncle Sabe there was their son, Paul, a tanned, strong, smooth-skinned young man with great energy for work and a patient kindness about him. There were my two sisters, June and Alberta, who spent those summers with me on the farm—five in all. And occasionally there were one or two other young children. I shall never be able to forget the breakfasts—the great flapjacks, which were made large enough to cover a whole dinner plate, just to save having to fork into the supply too often. I generally ate seven or eight of these monsters for breakfast, plus a couple of eggs and lots of fresh milk from the cow. And the dinners: serving dishes filled with mashed potatoes, carrots, string beans, peas, squash, and unforgettable ears of fresh corn. I remember, once, Paul and I competed against each other to see who could eat the greatest number of ears. I think I stopped at twelve, but I forget who won the race. It didn't matter, it was a memorable event, and we talked about it for some years. When Aunt Ruby made homemade doughnuts in an iron vat of boiling oil, we children stood expectantly beside the old-fashioned wood stove watching those golden brown delicacies as they were forked out and put on the heaping platter. Then we would gingerly take hold of one and try to eat it while it was still burning hot and melted in our mouths.

There was Spot, the dog—a lovely old English setter with sad, sweet eyes, a creature white with black spots streaked through his hair, hair that was often matted with nettles from the field and smelled of the accumulated odors of the farm. Spot was our great friend. You could hug him around the neck, you could play rough with him, you could do anything at all to that dog, and all you would get from him was loyalty and kindness. His great jaws dripped in the summer heat as he followed us everywhere. Uncle Sabe was of the opinion that Spot didn't amount to much as a dog; at least that's what he always said. He said Spot was the most useless hunting dog he'd ever seen—couldn't flush a woodchuck. But he could have gotten rid of that dog any time he wanted to, and yet he never did. When we sat out on the porch in the evening, Spot would lounge on the ground against the steps and listen to us, I suppose.

There is a great deal of my Mark Twain in Uncle Sabe. He had a kind of hidden humor that darted out of his blue eyes and I have not forgotten my delight in it because he wasn't a demonstrative man. He was a husky fellow, strong of build, deeply stained by the sun, and his face had rivulets of character cutting through it. His eyes, in particular, were framed by a delta of crinkling grooves. He had a soft Yankee drawl. His voice was deep. But the thing that characterized him most to me was the veiled humor that lurked in those eyes. And I think that the eyes of the Mark Twain I play are very much the eyes of my Uncle Sabe.

One of the dearest memories I have is the memory of those evenings on the porch. I don't recollect exactly the things that were said; I only remember the peace of it—the slow pace of it—the sounds and smells out there in the nestling shadows. The evening was a time when the day paused, when our life hung motionless in flight for a moment, when you could listen to the earth and hear it tick. There was excitement on that farm, too. There was adventure. When we had a thunderstorm, it was an adventure. We would dash for the truck with Paul, shouting, "Let me go too!" and careen down a bumpy dirt road out to the field where the chickens were, racing against the storm in order to round up the chickens and get them inside before they drowned in the flood of rain that always followed. Oh, what lightning we had in those days! I have never experienced thunder and lightning like that since. I loved to stand out on the porch and watch it and wonder when one of those bolts was going to crash to the ground in front of me.

I slept in a lumpy featherbed under the eaves in the large attic room. The bare shingles were over my head, and when it rained it was enchanting to have the sound of it so close to you. On clear nights the bluish moonlight poured in across the foot of my bed through the dormer window. Memories of this come back to me when I describe Mark Twain's boyhood room after the Ghost Story in Act Three.

There were three beautiful maple trees, great giants, lined up along the road beyond the incubator house and the flower garden (which was Aunt Ruby's pride). In the choicest of those three maples I built a tree-house. It was a retreat that was secure and safe and altogether romantic. It had a rope ladder that you could pull up after you, so that no pirate or Indian or outlaw or any of that breed could get at you. It was a good, sturdy tree-house, too. I took great care with the platform, building it across two tough limbs about twenty feet off the ground. It seems to me I slept out there on occasion, but maybe I just dreamed that.

There was a ritual we always went through when my

sisters and I arrived at the farm about the middle of June each year. We would tumble out of the car amidst the shouts and greetings, and Aunt Ruby would then hand me a pair of scissors. I would get out my new pair of overalls for that year. I would take the scissors and cut one pants-leg off above the knee, and then fringe it; cut the other leg off a little above the ankle and tatter the edge of that; pull off one strap, and then get down in the driveway dirt and roll. Once I had that pair of overalls humanized, I was ready for summer on the farm—barefoot, shirtless, rigged out in just that beautiful pair of overalls, with character; and that was all the costume I ever needed there.

The older I grow the more deeply I am convinced that when we get close to the soil of the earth we are in closer touch with the true spirit of life. Those were very satisfying days and I'll never be able to recapture them again, so the memory of them grows more and more precious to me. In *Mark Twain Tonight!* when Mark talks about his boyhood on his uncle's farm, I feel very close to understanding what he was trying to say. So often these days I remember his statement, "It makes me long for an elder time and a big toe with a rag around it." I think I know how he felt.

I have been to Hartford often and explored his magnificent home there. Into it Mark Twain poured one hundred thousand dollars, trying to satisfy his yearning for richness and grandeur. In one sense, it was Colonel Sellers all over again, a manifestation of the desire in Twain and in all of us to build the castle of our dreams. In this impressive home Mark Twain raised his family, lavishly entertained a succession of friends and celebrities, and retreated from one room to another in an effort to find the solitude he needed for his writing—finally settling in the third-floor billiard room.

Then, in the early 1890's, his castle tumbled down, his dreams exploded, and he left his sumptuous home behind in the wreckage of financial ruin and personal bereavement. The failure of his publishing house and his disastrous investment in the Paige Typesetter had bankrupted him. But the cruelest blow of all was the sudden death of a favorite daughter, Susy, a victim of spinal meningitis while he was going around the world on a lecture tour to help pay off his debts. From that time until the end of his life, he migrated from one place to another, "a wandering alien," seeking ... seeking as all men do for the answers that never come. If he was disillusioned by life, then he simply joined the ranks of millions of other men who have "lived, and longed, and hoped, and feared, and doubted." I am impatient with those critics who castigate Mark Twain for his pessimism as if it were some rare disease. It is a disease that infects us all. The thing to remember and admire is that Mark Twain left so much laughter behind. How many pessimists have done that?

One night I visited his grave in Elmira, where he lies beside those of his family who died before him: Langdon, his son; Susy and Jean, his daughters; Olivia, his wife. Langdon, Susy, and Jean died with terrible swiftness. His wife died after a long and pathetic illness during which he did everything in his power to save her. Each one of these tragedies wrought a deep hurt in him. He could not understand them or reconcile them with the justice and mercy of God as it is glorified in the pulpit. There seemed to be a contradiction in man's image of the Almighty, and he tried to reason it out. He could see no justice and mercy in a God who would strike down innocent children when it pleased him to do so. If God expected love and devotion from him, then he expected payment in kind. Something was amiss in

Man's conception of God, he reasoned. He was Job, seeking answers.

His commentary on religion and man's adherence to it was the result of tortured soul-searching and candid observation of the creature who labels himself "a Christian." His opinions are those of an honest-minded man. They are worth examining. You will note with what brilliance he inserts the blade of satire into the hearts of those one-day-a-week Christians who stand by and watch a lynching ("The United States of Lyncherdom" in Act Two). To Mark Twain a man was either *all* Christian or no Christian at all. It was a case of put up or shut up. He did not like phony holiness, and when he found it he exposed it with his choicest weapons—humor and satire—weapons more deadly than the sword. He once summed up his estimate of Man with these words: "The human race is a race of cowards; and I am not only marching in that procession, I am carrying a banner." It was like him to include himself.

One of the profoundest legacies Mark Twain has left us is his tolerance. It was not the pale, milky tolerance of the newly reformed, but a tolerance forged out of years of roughing it through the jungle of human experience. It derived from his observation of men and events and his conviction that the human race was a family and that each member of it should be judged for his worth and not by his color, creed, or origin. In an article entitled "Concerning the Jews" he wrote: "I am quite sure that I have no race prejudices, and I think I have no color prejudices nor caste prejudices nor creed prejudices. Indeed, I know it. I can stand any society. All that I care to know is that a man is a human being—that is good enough for me; he can't be any worse."

Twain's long friendship with the great Negro leader, Frederick Douglass, and his repeated championing of the Negro is most significant today in view of the efforts of small-minded men, white and black, who have tried to suppress *Huckleberry Finn* because it contains "references unfavorable to the Negro." Presumably, this phrase refers to his use of the word "nigger" and his portrait of our slave society in *Huckleberry Finn*.

Mark Twain was reared in a slave society. When he went east as a young man of eighteen to see the sights in New York, he wrote back: "These Eastern niggers are considerably better than white people." Yet ten years later, in San Francisco, he observed the stoning of a Chinese person and wrote a scorching indictment of the police of that city who stood by and watched. His newspaper refused to print the piece, but word of it reached the police chief, and eventually Twain had to leave town to escape his wrath. (It was then that he went up into the mountains for the winter and heard the Jumping Frog story—an interesting twist of fortune.) A few years later he was writing some savage editorials in the Buffalo *Express* on the subject of lynching, one of them headed "Only a Nigger," deploring the lynching of a Negro in Tennessee. Later, in *Huckleberry Finn*, he has Colonel Sherburn deliver a speech to a lynch mob that brilliantly cuts open the cowardice festering in this boil upon our national honor. And in 1901 he wrote "The United States of Lyncherdom," an unforgettable journalistic essay that should be required reading today in schools throughout the north and south. However, it is never mentioned so I have included it here, in Act Two.

It is one thing to be taught from infancy that race prejudice is undesirable and unworthy, as many of us are trying to teach our children today. But it is quite another thing to *begin* with a built-in prejudice and grow up and get rid of it, as Mark Twain got rid of his years ago, before it became fashionable to be unprejudiced. In our own efforts to grow up, it would be more than unfortunate if we allowed a great literary achievement like *Huckleberry Finn* to be suppressed because it shows us as we *were* one hundred and more years ago. Yet we have allowed it—the book has been suppressed, notably by the school board of New York City. This is a strange road to enlightenment. Is it too much to ask that the use of the word "nigger" and the reasons for slavery be *explained* to the students? Use *Huck Finn* as the text; the book is nothing less than a hymn to brotherhood, as anyone —boy or man—can discover by reading it.

When it came time to do the recording of *Mark Twain Tonight!* there was a good deal of discussion about the advisability of leaving in "Pap's" speech about the "free nigger from Ohio" in the *Huckleberry Finn* selection. It was feared this might hurt the sale of the record. In fact, we needed to cut three minutes from that side of the record and "Pap's" speech would have done the job neatly. But we decided not to cut it, after all. I knew Governor Long down in Louisiana would enjoy it, anyway, and I did not wish to disappoint him.

Late in his life Mark Twain wrote a letter to a girl in France, a member of the club he had formed which consisted of young girls, one from each country, who wrote him letters on various subjects and received his replies. As he put it: "I do not represent a country myself, but am merely Member at Large for the Human Race." We may consider this his final comment on the subject of racial prejudice, for it was written at "Stormfield," Redding, Connecticut, on August 26, 1909, less than a year before he died. It was reprinted in the *Ladies' Home Journal* for February, 1912.

Dear France:

It was a lovely picture, dear France. Nothing else in the world is ever so beautiful as a beautiful schoolgirl, and certainly there is a prodigal wealth of that beauty in this picture. This Joan [of Arc] is to my taste—fair, and comely, and sweet, and refined; whereas four artists out of five make Joan coarse and clumsy, and thirty or forty years old. They seem to think that because she was a peasant she couldn't have been otherwise. Then they spoil the argument by making the Virgin Mary, who was also a peasant, fair, and comely, and sweet, and refined—and *white*. Which she wasn't. . . .

P.S. I've broken the letter open for a reason that moves me to laugh. When the stenographer had typed it he placed it, with other letters, on my daughter Jean's desk (she is my secretary), and she read it. She went driving afterward, and I prepared the letter for the mail. But as soon as she returned she brought it to me and said I must open it and *change* something in it.

"Well, Jean, what must I change?"

"You have said the Virgin Mary was not white."

"Very well, where's the harm?"

"Why, it's shocking!"

"You numskull! What is there about it that's shocking?"

"Can't you see, Papa? The idea of saying the Mother of the Saviour was *colored!* It's sacrilegious."

"Sac—oh, nonsense! Jean, in her day the population of the globe was not more than a thousand millions. Not *one-tenth* of them were *white*. What does this fact suggest to you?"

"I—I don't know. What does it suggest, Papa?"

"It most powerfully suggests that white was not a favorite complexion with God. Has it since become a favorite complexion with Him? No. The population of the globe is now fifteen hundred millions; one thousand and six millions of these people are *colored*—two-thirds, you see, of the human race. There was not a white person in Nazareth when I was there, except a foreign priest. The people were very dark. Don't you suppose they are the descendants of Mary's townsmen? Of course they are. Now what have you to say, Jean?"

"Well, I can't help it, Papa; the idea of a colored Mother of the Saviour is still *revolting*, and you must change it."

"My dear, I won't. To my mind one color is just as respectable as another; there is nothing important, nothing essential, about a complexion. I mean, to *me*. But with the Deity it is different. He doesn't think much of white people. He prefers the colored. Andrea del Sarto's pink-and-lily Madonnas revolt Him, my child. That is, they *would*, but He never looks at them."

I am not writing this Prologue for scholars. I am writing it with the urgent hope that Members at Large of the Human Race will be curious enough to read through it and get to the good part, which begins shortly, and have a wonderful time.

But, lest I incur the wrath of a good many parishioners in the congregation of St. Mark, let me explain that the selections in this volume have been edited for the stage. I have taken liberties with the authentic text in some places which are bound to dismay certain scholars. And my sympathy is with them. Others, perhaps, will realize that in putting together a dramatic adaptation of any kind, whether the cast requires one actor or ten, there must be a great deal of selection done, and in the case of this collection a great deal of editorial splicing.

Wherever possible, I have stuck to the original text except for cutting it down to stage size, as in the long *Huckleberry Finn* selection and the satiric burlesque on the Evolution of Man. In selections such as the satire on the missionaries to the Sandwich Islands and the German Opera and How to Be Seventy routines, I have taken pieces of the original text and swapped them around and mixed them up with other stories so that you will have tough sledding if you go back to the original and match it against any of these. This is the character of the work I have done throughout the three acts. The material has been tested in this form in front of audiences, and this is the way it plays best, in my opinion.

I was relieved to find that Mark Twain did much the same thing. Not only did he use a good story three or four times, in different contexts, as in the case of the "Watermelon Story" (Act Three), he also cut his original material for use on the platform (his lecture version of the Jumping Frog is shorter than mine) and even departed freely from his original text. He explains some of his methods in Bernard De Voto's *Mark Twain in Eruption* by using the example of "His Grandfather's Old Ram." He told this story on the platform for several years, starting out by referring to the book and then realizing that this system eliminated his most powerful tool—the Pause. The "reader" cannot get the effect out of it that the pure storyteller can. Years later, when he tried reading the story from *Roughing It* to a group of friends, he found "it wouldn't read." So he did it from memory. The difference between the story he told from memory and the version in the book startled him so that he wrote the former down. I have used most of it in my version of the "Ram."

But let me make one thing clear—*I do not improvise his stories.* I tell them from memory, and try to make it *sound* like improvisation. I do not ad lib, except in emergencies, such as when the fly flew on stage.

In order to aid anyone attempting to check the accuracy of my material, I have used those slim little footnote numbers at the end of every selection throughout the three acts, and if he has the energy left for it he can look back in the rear of the book and find the source for that phrase, line, anecdote, or full story. By this inspection he will under-

stand why it has taken me so many years to put this material together. I hope. And I hope just as fervently that the
general reader will ignore the little numbers and read straight
through without fear or misgiving.

Certain readers will curse me for not putting titles at the
beginning of each story. I apologize. I did it because I do
not want to give you the entertainment of picking through
a table of contents and choosing the titles you like best and
ignoring those that do not strike your fancy. My purpose is
to allow Mark Twain to tell you a story about himself and
his times, his likes and dislikes, the things he laughed at and
the things he loved, his hopes, his doubts, his estimate of the
whole animal kingdom from the Amalekite to Man. I have
divided the material into three acts because it is supposed
to be a compilation of the repertoire of my show. I want to
make it clear—*very clear*—that I do not do *all* of this material in one night and on one show. If that damaging impression got around I would have to store my white wig and
suit in mothballs. What you have here represents about five
times the amount of material I would do on any given evening—maybe four times.

Mark Twain once described his method of constructing
a lecture by using the illustration of a peg board. The peg
board had a series of holes in it—round, square, triangular,
and all in the same sequence. For instance, the first peg
hole would always be a round one, the second one also
round, the third square, the fourth triangular, and so on
through the lecture. The sequence was always the same. In
his pockets, figuratively speaking, he had an oversupply of
round, square, and triangular pegs. Now as he went along
in the lecture, sounding out the audience, he would choose
from among the round pegs the one that he felt would
achieve the best effect and jam it in the hole. When he got

to the next hole which, let us say, was square he would fish into his supply of square pegs and pick out the one most likely to rouse that particular audience. Same routine with the triangulars. Do you follow me? Then read it over again because the hard part is coming up.

Each one of the selections in Acts One, Two, and Three represents a round, square, or triangular peg. Selections are indicated by a double space—the end of a round peg, say, and the beginning of a square. Have you got that? Well, read it over again. Now in certain cases two, three, or four pegs are stuck together between my double spaces because, well—wouldn't it be silly to interrupt the flow of all that Huckleberry Finn material too often, for instance? Yet, the entire Huck Finn selection represents a good four pegs—triangular. I am never really sure which one of them I will do on stage until I am ready to start the selection. It helps keep the show fresh and surprising.

Two years ago in Hannibal when I saw the brief Thomas Edison film of Mark Twain for the first time, I was fearful. I had worked many years to create the character, mainly by intuition and research, and now I was to receive a verdict. The film flickered into action; I saw him before me and experienced a jolt of delightful recognition. There was no sound, just the jaunty pantomime of this old friend passing in review, but I laughed and laughed until I felt good all over. To those of you who know Mark Twain and love him, I hope there is delightful recognition awaiting you. To those who are about to meet him for the first time—relax ... the world is really going to survive. Read and you'll see what I mean.

41st STREET THEATRE

JOHN LOTAS in association with BUNKER JENKINS

presents

HAL HOLBROOK

in

"MARK TWAIN TONIGHT!"

PROGRAMME

Note: While Mr. Twain's selections will come from the list below, we have been unable to pin him down as to which of them he will do. He claims this would cripple his inspiration. However, he has generously conceded to a printed programme for the benefit of those who are in distress and wish to fan themselves.

The Dangers of Abstinence	*Following The Equator*
The Italian Guide	*Innocents Abroad*
The Genuine Mexican Plug	*Roughing It*
Advice To Youth	*Speeches*
Encounter With An Interviewer	*Short Story*
The Great French Duel	*A Tramp Abroad*
Accident Insurance	*Speeches*
Poet Story	*Speeches*
Buck Fanshaw's Funeral	*Roughing It*
The Watermelon Story	*Speeches*
The Celebrated Jumping Frog	*Short Story*
Awful German Language	*A Tramp Abroad*
Taming The Bicycle	*Short Story*
Grandfather's Old Ram	*Roughing It*
Cadets of Temperance	*Tom Sawyer*
The Shooting of Boggs	*Huckleberry Finn*
My Ancestor Satan	*Short Stories*
My Trained Presbyterian Conscience	*Autobiography*
How To Give Up Smoking	*Miscellaneous*
Sandwich Islands	*Roughing It*
The Ant: An Imposter	*A Tramp Abroad*
Huck and Jim	*Huckleberry Finn*
Colonel Sellers and the Turnips	*The Gilded Age*
Politics	*Miscellaneous*
The German Opera	*A Tramp Abroad*
Success	*Miscellaneous*
On Talking	*Speeches*
A Ghost Story	*Short Story*
I Took Along the Window Sash	*Innocents Abroad*
How To Be Seventy	*Speeches*
How I Stole My Name	*Life On The Mississippi*

Intermissions: Two, probably.

Music: A trombone player was engaged, but is unreliable and should not be expected.

Facsimile of the program for Hal Holbrook's New York engagement April 6, 1959, to September 6, 1959. The text that follows in this book contains all the above selections, together with many more that Mr. Holbrook does not usually use on the stage.

Act One

Ladies and gentlemen, I wish to present to you a man whose great learning and veneration for truth are only exceeded by his high moral character and majestic presence. I refer in these vague, general terms to myself.

I consider introductions unnecessary but if it is the custom to have them, I prefer to do the act myself, so that I can rely on getting in all the facts.[1] I was born modest but it wore off.[2]

I was once presented to an audience by a lawyer, who kept his hands in his pockets. He introduced me as "Mark Twain, a humorist who is really funny—a very rare creature, indeed." Why, I was struck speechless by this complimentary thunderbolt. I had scarcely in my lifetime listened to a compliment so beautifully phrased, or so well deserved.[3] But we had a much rarer creature in our midst than a humorist who was really funny. We had a lawyer who kept his hands in his own pockets.[4]

Oh, but I do like compliments. We all do; humorists, burglars, congressmen—all of us in the trade.[5] The plan of the newspaper is good. If you can't get a compliment any other way, pay yourself one.[6] I do that often. I can do it right now; I can state at this moment that there are two men who are

101

most remarkable: Kipling is one and I am the other one. Between us we cover all knowledge. He knows all that can be known, and I know the rest.[7]

I collect them, too. I have a compliment collection, so that I can take them out and look at them every once in a while. And I've brought some of them along. Now the first one of these lies is by my biographer, Albert Bigelow Paine. He's writing four octava volumes about me and he has been at my elbow for two and a half years. Now I just suppose that he does not know me. But he says he knows me. He says: "Mark Twain is not only a great writer, a great philosopher, a great man, he is the supreme expression of the human being, with every human strength! And weakness." What a talent for compression.[8] I've been charged with having no reverence for anything, but I have reverence for a man who can utter the truth like that—as far as it goes.[9]

Now here is the compliment of a little Montana girl, which came to me indirectly. She was in a room in which there was a large photograph of me on the wall, and after gazing at it steadily for a time she said: "We've got a picture of John the Baptist, too. Only ours has got more trimmings." I suppose she meant the halo.[10]

Now, ladies and gentlemen, I hope you won't mind if I smoke. I believe there is some commandment against smoking during insurrections of this dignified nature; but I am working to get it removed. Mind you, I have no objections to abstinence, as long as it does not harm anybody. I practice it myself, on occasion.[11] I make it a rule never to smoke when asleep. Not that I care for moderation myself. I do it as an example to others, and to prove that I am not a slave to the habit.[12] I can give it up whenever I want to. I've done it a thousand times.[13]

The first time I gave it up was when I was a boy about ten or eleven. They told me that I would shorten my life ten years by smoking, so I got scared and gave it up one day. Then I decided the decade wouldn't be worth living without any smoking in it, so that was the end of that.[14]

Another time I joined the Cadets of Temperance and took the pledge. The Cadets of Temperance had a uniform with a bright red sash, and I believe it was that sash which reformed me. I could scarcely wait for the Fourth of July so that I might wear it in the parade. But the Fourth was too long in coming; I gave up waiting for that and pinned my hopes on old Judge Frazier, who was apparently on his deathbed and was sure to have a big public funeral—with a procession.

I was deeply concerned about the Judge's condition, and hungry for news of it. But he had the most discouraging way of fluctuating. He got better, then worse, then better again. It seemed to me he was overdoing the thing. Finally he was pronounced cured. I felt injured. I handed in my resignation to the Cadets of Temperance and resumed my cigar.

And that night the Judge had a relapse and died.[15]

Years later I gave it up again, on the advice of my doctor. I had been confined to my bed for several days, with the lumbago, and the doctor finally said to me, "Look here, my remedies haven't got a chance. Consider what they have to fight besides the lumbago: you smoke extravagantly; you eat all manner of things that don't agree with each other's company; you drink two hot scotches every night, don't you?"[16]

I said, "Yes I do, but I only drink them as a preventative

of toothache. I've never had the toothache. And I don't ever intend to have it." [17]

He said, "That's all right, but we can't make any progress that way. You've got to moderate those things."

"I can't do it, doctor."

"Why can't you?"

"Because I lack the will power. I can cut 'em off entirely but I can't moderate them."

He said that would answer, so I cut off all those things for two days and two nights and at the end of that time the lumbago was discouraged and left me. I was a well man again. So I gave thanks and took to these delicacies again.

It seemed a good system, so I recommended this remedy to an elderly lady friend of mine. She'd gone down and down to the point where medicines no longer had any helpful effect on her. I told her I could cure her in a week. I said she must give up smoking, and drinking, and eating and swearing, and by the end of the week she'd be on her feet. Why, she said she couldn't give up smoking and drinking and swearing because she'd never done any of those things! So there it was. She'd neglected her habits. She was a sinking ship with no freight to throw overboard. Why, just one or two little bad habits would have saved her; but she was just a moral pauper.[18]

When I was a young man, studying for the gallows,[19] I went west on the Overland Stage to seek my fortune in the silverland of the Nevada territory. My brother had been appointed Secretary of the new territory. I was young and ignorant, and I envied him the long, strange journey he was going to make. He would see buffaloes and Indians and deserts and have all kinds of adventures, and maybe get hanged or scalped, and write home and tell us all about it. And he would see gold and silver mines, and maybe go out in the afternoon when his work was done and pick up two or three pailfuls of gold and silver nuggets. So when he offered me, in cold blood, the sublime position of private secretary under him, I was packed and ready for the journey in an hour.

It took six days to go from St. Louis to "St. Joe" by steamboat. The trip was a confused jumble of savage-looking snags which we deliberately walked over with one wheel or the other; and of sand-bars which we roosted on occasionally, and rested, and then got out our crutches and sparred over. The boat might almost as well have gone to St. Joe by land, she was walking most of the time. She was a good boat, but a pair of stilts would have improved her.[20]

I was armed to the teeth with a pitiful little Smith & Wesson's seven-shooter. It carried a ball like a homeopathic pill, but it appeared to me a dangerous weapon. It had only one fault—you could not hit anything with it. I practiced awhile on a cow and as long as she stood still and behaved herself she was safe. But as soon as she went to moving around and I got to shooting at other things, she came to grief.

Our fellow passenger, Bemis, carried an old original Allen revolver—sometimes called a "pepper box." Bemis went after a deuce of spades nailed against a tree, once, and fetched a mule standing about thirty yards to the left of it. Bemis did not want the mule; but the owner came out with a shotgun and persuaded him to buy it, anyhow. It was a comprehensive weapon—the "Allen." When all six barrels went off at once there was no safe place but behind it.[21]

At eight o'clock on a superb summer morning we jumped into the stage, stretched out on the mail sacks, the driver cracked his whip, and we bowled away. The stage whirled along at a spanking gait, the breeze flapping curtains and suspended coats in a most exhilarating way; we swayed and swung luxuriously, the cracking of the driver's whip, and his "Hi-yi! g'long!" were music. The spinning ground and the waltzing trees appeared to give us a mute hurrah as we went by, and then slack up and look after us with interest, or envy, or something. As we lay and smoked the pipe of peace and compared all this luxury with the years of tiresome city life that had gone before it, we felt that there was only one complete and satisfying happiness in the world, and we had found it.

About five hundred and fifty miles from St. Joseph, our chariot broke down. We were going to be delayed five or six hours, so we took horses and joined a party who were just starting on a buffalo hunt. It was a noble sport galloping over the plain in the dewy freshness of the morning, but our part of the hunt ended in disaster and disgrace. A wounded buffalo bull chased Bemis nearly two miles until he forsook the horse and took to a tree. He was pretty sullen about the whole matter for some twenty-four hours, but at last he began to soften little by little, and finally he said:

"Well, it was not funny. I wish you fellows had been up the tree; you wouldn't have wanted to laugh so. If I'd had a horse worth a cent—but no, the minute he saw that bull wheel on him and give a bellow, he raised straight up in the air and stood on his heels. I took him round the neck and began to pray. Then he came down and stood up on the other end awhile, and the bull actually stopped bellowing and pawing sand just to contemplate the inhuman spectacle. Then the bull made a pass at him and uttered a bellow that sounded perfectly frightful, it was so close to me, and that seemed to literally prostrate my horse's reason, and I wish I may die if he didn't stand on his head for a quarter of a minute and shed tears. He was absolutely out of his mind. Then

the bull came charging at us, and that horse dropped down
on all fours and took a fresh start—and for the next ten minutes he threw one handspring after another so fast the bull
began to get unsettled, too. He didn't know where to start in.
He stood there sneezing, and shoveling dust over his back,
thinking he'd got a fifteen-hundred dollar circus horse for
breakfast, certain. Well, I was first out on his neck, then
underneath, and next on his rump—I tell you it was solemn
and awful to be ripping and tearing and carrying on so in
the presence of death, as you might say. The bull made a
snatch for us and brought away some of my horse's tail, and
then you ought to have seen that spider-legged old skeleton
go! and you ought to have seen the bull cut out after him, too
—head down, tongue out, tail up, mowing down the weeds,
and boosting up the sand like a whirlwind! By George, it was
a hot race! I and the saddle were back on the rump, and I
had the bridle in my teeth and was holding on to the pommel
with both hands. We left the dogs behind; we passed a jackass rabbit; we overtook a cayote, and were gaining on an
antelope when the rotten girths let go and threw me about
thirty yards off to the left, and as the saddle went down over
the horse's rump he gave it a lift with his heels that sent it
more than four hundred yards up in the air, I wish I may die
in a minute if he didn't. I fell at the foot of the only solitary
tree in nine counties adjacent, and the next second I had hold
of the bark with four sets of nails and my teeth, and the next
second after that I was astraddle of the main limb.

"I *had* the bull, now, if he did not think of *one* thing. But
that one thing I dreaded. I dreaded it very seriously. There
was a possibility that the bull might not think of it, but there
were greater chances that he would. I made up my mind
what I would do in case he did. It was a little over forty feet

to the ground from where I sat. I cautiously unwound the
lariat from the pommel of my saddle—"

"Your *saddle?* Did you take your saddle up in the tree
with you?"

"Take it up in the tree with me? Of course I didn't. It *fell*
in the tree when it came down."

"Oh."

"Certainly. I unwound the lariat, and fastened one end
of it to the limb. It was the very best green raw-hide, and
capable of sustaining tons. I made a slip-noose in the other
end, and then hung it down to see the length. It reached
down twenty-two feet—half way to the ground. I then loaded
every barrel of the Allen with a double charge. I felt
satisfied. I said to myself, if he never thinks of that one
thing that I dread, all right—but if he does, I am fixed for
him. I watched the bull, now, with anxiety. Presently a
thought came into the bull's eye. I knew it! Sure enough,
it was just as I had dreaded, he started in to climb the tree—"

"The bull?"

"Of course—who else?"

"But a bull can't climb a tree."

"He can't, can't he? Since you know so much about it,
did you ever see a bull try?"

"No!"

"Well, because you never saw a thing done, is that any
reason why it can't be done?"

"Well, all right—go on. What did you do?"

"The bull started up, and got along well for about
ten feet, then slipped and slid back. I breathed easier. He
tried it again—got up a little higher—slipped again. But
he came at it once more, and this time he was careful. Up he
came—an inch at a time—with his eyes hot, and his tongue
hanging out. Higher and higher—hitched his foot over the

stump of a limb, and looked up, as much as to say, 'You are
my meat, friend.' Up again—higher and higher, and getting
more excited the closer he got. He was within ten feet of me!
I took a long breath, and then said I, 'It is now or never.'
I had the coil of the lariat all ready; I paid it out slowly,
till it hung right over his head; all of a sudden I let go of
the slack and the slip-noose fell fairly round his neck!
Quicker than lightning I out with the Allen and let him have
it in the face. It was an awful roar, and must have scared
the bull out of his senses. When the smoke cleared away,
there he was, dangling in the air, twenty foot from the
ground, and going out of one convulsion into another faster
than you could count! I didn't stop to count, anyhow—
I shinned down the tree and shot for home."

"Bemis, is all that true, just as you have stated it?"

"I wish I may rot in my tracks and die the death of a
dog if it isn't."

"Well, we can't refuse to believe it, and we don't. But
if there were some proofs—"

"Proofs! Did I bring back my lariat?"

"No."

"Did I bring back my horse?"

"No."

"Did you ever see the bull again?"

"No."

"Well, then, what more do you want?" [22]

I made up my mind that if this man was not a liar
he would become one if he kept on.[23]

"*HERE SHE COMES!*"
Every neck is stretched further, and every eye strained

wider. Away across the endless dead level of the prairie a
black speck appears against the sky, and it is plain that it
moves. In a second or two it becomes a horse and rider,
rising and falling, rising and falling—sweeping toward us
nearer and nearer—growing more and more distinct, more
and more sharply defined—nearer and still nearer, and the
flutter of the hoofs comes faintly to the ear—another instant
a whoop and a hurrah from our upper deck, a wave of
the rider's hand, but no reply, and man and horse burst
past our excited faces, and go winging away like a belated
fragment of a storm!

So sudden is it all, and so like a flash of unreal fancy,
that but for the flake of white foam left quivering and
perishing on a mail-sack after the vision had flashed by
and disappeared, we might have doubted whether we had
seen any actual horse and man at all, maybe. This was
the "pony-rider"—the fleet messenger who sped across the
continent from St. Joe to Sacramento, carrying letters
nineteen hundred miles in eight days." [24]

Our stay in Salt Lake City amounted to only two days,
so there wasn't the time to make the customary inquisition
into the workings of polygamy, and get up the usual statistics,
preparatory to calling the attention of the nation at large
once more to the matter. I had the will to do it. Oh, yes.
With the gushing self-sufficiency of youth, I was feverish to
plunge in and achieve a great reform there, until I saw the
Mormon women. Then I was touched. My heart was wiser
than my head. It warmed toward those poor, ungainly,
pathetically homely creatures, and as I turned to hide the
generous moisture in my eye, I thought "No, the man that
marries one of them has done an act of Christian charity,
which entitles him to the kindly applause of mankind, not

their harsh censure—and the man that marries sixty of them has done a deed of open-handed generosity so sublime that the nations should stand uncovered in his presence, and worship in silence."

A man named Johnson told me of a conversation he professed to have had with Brigham Young. He said that Mr. Young told him marriage was "a perfect dog's life. You can't economize. It isn't possible! Why, the wash bill alone—nine hundred and eighty-four pieces a week! And cradles—think of it! And soothing syrup! Teething rings! And 'pap's watches' for the babies to play with! And things to scratch the furniture with! And matches for them to eat, and pieces of glass to cut themselves with! The item of glass alone would support your whole family, I dare say. Let me scrimp and squeeze all I can, I can't get ahead.

"Why, bless you, sir, at a time when I had seventy-two wives in this house, I groaned under the pressure of keeping thousands of dollars tied up in seventy-two bedsteads, when the money ought to have been out at interest. And I just sold out the whole stock, sir, at a sacrifice, and built a bedstead seven feet long and ninety-six feet wide. But it was a failure, sir. I could *not* sleep. It appeared to me that the whole seventy-two women snored at once. The roar was deafening. And then the danger of it. That was what I was looking at. They would all draw in their breath at once, and you could actually see the walls of the house suck in—and then they would all exhale, and you could see the walls swell out, and strain, and hear the rafters crack, and the shingles grind together. My friend, take an old man's advice, and *don't* encumber yourself with a large family. Don't do it. Take my word for it, ten or eleven wives is all you need—never go over it."

Some instinct or other made me set this Johnson down as being unreliable.²⁵

On the evening of the nineteenth day we came to Nevada and halted at Ragtown on the western edge of the Great American Desert. The country looked something like a singed cat.²⁶ There wasn't a living creature within fifty miles, except a few stray Indians, some crippled grasshoppers, and four or five buzzards out of meat and too feeble to get away.²⁷ There is a popular tradition that the Almighty created Nevada, but when you come to see it you will think differently.²⁸

We crossed the Carson River, a moist ditch which is the counterpart of the Erie in all respects save that the canal is twice as long and four times as deep. If it was my river I wouldn't leave it outdoors nights, in this careless way, where any dog can come along and lap it up.²⁹

I eventually located in Virginia City, which was a good place for a man to lose his religion, if he had any left by the time he got there.³⁰

Virginia had grown to be the livest town, for its age and population, that America had ever produced. The great Comstock Lode stretched its opulent length straight through the town from north to south. Money was as plentiful as dust. There was a glad, almost fierce intensity in every eye, the kind of a look a man has when he is counting his money. There were brass bands, fire companies, banks, hotels, theaters, wide-open gambling places, civic processions, street fights, murders, riots, a whiskey mill every fifteen steps, a half-dozen jails, and some talk of building a church. It was no place for a Presbyterian, and I did not remain one very long.

Now one of my strongest memories of those flush times in Virginia is Buck Fanshaw's funeral. There was a grand time over Buck Fanshaw when he died. He was a representative citizen. He had killed his man—not in his own quarrel, but in defense of a stranger unfairly beset by numbers. He'd kept a sumptuous saloon. He'd been the proprietor of a dashing helpmate whom he could have discarded without the formality of a divorce. He'd held a high position in the fire department and had been a very Warwick in politics.

On the inquest it was shown that Buck Fanshaw, in the delirium of typhoid fever, had taken arsenic, shot himself through the body, cut his throat, and jumped out of a four-story window and broken his neck, and after due deliberation the jury brought in a verdict of death "by the visitation of God." What could the world do without juries?

Prodigious preparations were made for the funeral. All the vehicles in town were hired, all the saloons were put in mourning, all the municipal and fire company flags hung at half-mast, and the firemen ordered to muster in uniform and bring their machines duly draped in black.

Now let me remark here that the slang of Nevada was the richest and most infinitely varied that had ever existed anywhere in the world, perhaps. Slang was the language of Nevada. It was hard to preach a sermon without it and be understood.

A committee of one was deputed to call on the minister, a fragile, gentle new fledgling from an Eastern theological seminary. The committeeman, "Scotty" Bridges, made his visit. His face was the picture of woe. He sat down before the clergyman, placed his fire-hat on an unfinished sermon, took from it a red silk handkerchief, wiped his brow, and heaved a sigh. He choked and even shed tears. But with an effort he mastered his voice and said:

"Are you the duck that runs the gospel-mill next door?"

"Am I the—pardon me, I believe I do not understand?"

"Why, you see we're in a bit of trouble and the boys thought maybe you'd give us a lift, if we'd tackle you—that is, if I've got the rights of it and you are the head clerk of the doxology works next door."

"I am the shepherd in charge of the flock whose fold is next door."

"The which?"

"The spiritual adviser of the little company of believers whose sanctuary adjoins these premises."

"I recken I can't call that hand."

"I beg pardon."

"Well, you've ruther got the bulge on me. Or maybe we've both got the bulge, somehow. You see, one of the boys has passed in his checks and we want to give him a good send-off, and so the thing I'm on now is to roust out somebody to jerk a little chin-music for us and waltz him through handsome."

"My friend, I seem to grow more and more bewildered. At first I thought perhaps I misunderstood you, but I grope now. Would it not expedite matters if you restricted yourself to categorical statements of fact, unencumbered with obstructing accumulations of metaphor and allegory?"

"I'll have to pass, I judge."

"How?"

"You've raised me out, pard. That last lead of yourn is too many for me. I can't neither trump nor follow suit."

The clergyman sank back in his chair perplexed. Scotty leaned his head on his hand and gave himself up to thought. Presently his face came up, sorrowful but confident.

"I've got it now, so's you can savvy. What we want is a gospel-sharp. See?"

"A what?"

"Gospel-sharp. Parson."

"Oh! Why did you not say so before? I am a clergyman—
a parson."

"Now you talk. Put it there!" His paw closed over the
minister's small hand and squeezed the blood right out of
it. "Now we're all right, pard. Let's start fresh. Don't
you mind my snuffling a little—becuz we're in a power of
trouble. You see, one of the boys has gone up the flume—"

"Gone . . . where?"

"Up the flume—throwed up the sponge, you understand?"

"Thrown up the sponge?"

"Yes—kicked the bucket—"

"Ah—has departed to that mysterious country from whose
bourne no traveller returns."

"Return! I reckon not. Why, pard, he's *dead!*"

"Yes, I understand."

"You do? Well, I thought you might be getting tangled
up some more. Yes, you see he's dead again—"

"Again! Why, has he ever been dead before?"

"Dead before? No! But you bet he's awful dead now,
poor old boy, and if we can get you to help plant him—"

"Preach the funeral discourse? Assist at the obsequies?"

"Obs'quies is good. Yes, that's it. That's our little game.
We're going to get the thing up regardless, you know.
And we'll take care of you, too. Put Buck through as bully
as you can, pard, for anybody that knowed him will tell you
that he was one of the whitest men that was ever in the
mines. You can't draw it too strong. He never could stand
to see things going wrong. He's done more to make this
town quiet and peaceable than any man in it. If a thing
wanted regulating, he warn't a man to go browsing around
after somebody to do it, but he would prance in and regulate

it himself. He warn't a Catholic, scasely. He was down on
'em. His word was 'No Irish need apply!' But it didn't make
no difference about that when it came down to what a man's
rights were—so, when some roughs jumped the Catholic bone-
yard and started in to stake out town lots on it, he *went* for
'em! And he *cleaned* 'em, too! I was there, pard, and I seen it
myself."

"That was very well, indeed—at least the impulse was—
whether the act was strictly defensible or not. Had deceased
any religious convictions? That is to say, did he feel a dependence upon, or acknowledge allegiance to a higher power?"

"Could you say it over once more, and say it slow?"

"Well, to simplify it somewhat, was he, or rather had he
ever been connected with any organization sequestered from
secular concerns and devoted to self-sacrifice in the interests
of morality?"

"All down but nine—set 'em up on the other alley, pard."

"What did I understand you to say?"

"Why, you're most too many for me, you know. When you
get in with your left I hunt grass ever time. Evertime you
draw, you fill; but I don't seem to have any luck. Let's have
a new deal."

"How? Begin again?"

"That's it."

"Very well. Was he a good man, and—"

"There—I see that! Don't put up another chip till I look at
my hand. A good man, says you? Pard, it ain't no name for it.
He was the best man that ever—pard, you would have doted
on that man. He could lam any galoot of his inches in America. It was him that put down the riot last election before
it got a start; and everybody said he was the only man that
could a done it. He sent fourteen men home on a shutter in
less than three minutes. He had the riot all broke up and

prevented nice, before anybody got a chance to strike a blow. He was always for peace, and he would *have* peace—he could not stand disturbances. Pard, he was a great loss to this town. It would please the boys if you could chip in something like that and do him justice. And you can say, pard, that he never shook his mother."

"Never shook his mother?"

"That's it—any of the boys will tell you so."

"Well, but why *should* he shake her?"

"That's what *I* say. But some people does."

"Not people of any repute? In my opinion the man that would offer personal violence to his own mother, ought to—"

"Cheese it, pard; you've banked your ball clean outside the string. What I was driving at was that he never *throwed off* on his mother—don't you see? He give her a house to live in, and town lots, and plenty of money; and he looked after her and took care of her all the time. And when she was down with the smallpox I'm damned if he didn't set up nights and nuss her himself! *Beg* your pardon for saying it, but it hopped out too quick for yours truly. You've treated me like a gentleman, pard, and I ain't the man to hurt your feelings intentional. I think you're white. I think you're a square man, pard. I like you, and I'll lick any man that don't. I'll lick him till he can't tell himself from a last year's corpse! Put it there!"

The obsequies were all that "the boys" could desire. Such a marvel of funeral pomp had never been seen in Virginia City, and for years afterwards the degree of grandeur attained by any civic display in Virginia City was determined by comparison with Buck Fanshaw's funeral.

Scotty Bridges, in after days, achieved the distinction of becoming the only convert to religion that was ever gathered from the Virginia City roughs. And it turned out that he was of no mean timber whereof to construct a Christian. The making him one did not warp his generosity or diminish his courage. On the contrary, it gave intelligent direction to the one and a broader field to the other. If his Sunday-school class progressed faster than the other classes, was it a matter of wonder? I think not. He talked to his pioneer-fry in a language they understood! It was my privilege, a month before he died, to hear him tell the beautiful story of Joseph and his brethren to his Sunday-school class "without looking at the book." I leave it to you to fancy what it was like, as it fell, riddled with slang, from the lips of that grave, earnest teacher, and was listened to by his little learners with a consuming interest that showed that they were as unconscious as he was that any violence was being done to the sacred proprieties! [31]

Like everyone else I was smitten with the silver fever. My comrades and I went out prospecting—we climbed the mountainsides among the sage brush, rocks, and snow; day after day we toiled and climbed and searched; and finally we located a claim. My comrades dug a shaft on it eight feet deep, and then I went down with a long-handled shovel to throw out the loose dirt. I made the toss, landed the mess just on the edge of the shaft, and it all came back on my head and settled inside my clothes. I climbed out of the hole and walked home. [32]

I never ceased to expect that a fortune would burst upon me some day. Meanwhile I had to eat and save up my strength for it, so I presently went to work as a common laborer in a quartz mill at ten dollars a week and board. [33]

I was the most careful workman they ever had. They said so. I took more pains with my work. I was shoveling sand. Whenever I had a lot of sand to shovel, I was so particular that I would sit down an hour and a half and think about the best way to shovel that sand. And if I could not cipher it out in my mind just so, I would not go shoveling it around needless. I would leave it alone till next day. Why, many a time when I would be carrying a bucketful of sand from one pile to another, thirty or forty feet off, right in the middle a new idea would suddenly strike me and I would carry that sand back and sit down and think about it, and like as not get so wrought up and absorbed in it that I would go to sleep. Why, I always knew there must be some tip-top, first-rate way to move that sand.

And at last I discovered it. I went to the boss and told him that I had got just the thing, the very best and quickest way to get that sand from one pile to the other, and he said:

"I'm awful, awful glad to hear it."

You never saw a man so uplifted as he was. I said:

"What you want now is a cast-iron pipe about thirteen or fourteen feet in diameter, and say forty feet long. And you want to prop up one end of that pipe about thirty-five or forty feet off the ground. And then you want a revolving belt—with a revolving chair in it. I am to sit in that chair and have somebody down there to fill up the bucket with sand and pass it up. And as I come around, I am just to soar up there and tilt it into that pipe, and there you are. It is as easy as rolling off a log!"

I only remained in the milling business one week.[34]

Every now and then, in these days, the boys used to tell me I ought to get old Jim Blaine to tell me the stirring story of his grandfather's old ram—but they always added that I must not mention the matter unless Jim was drunk at the time— just comfortably and socially drunk. I got to haunting Blaine; but it was of no use, the boys always found fault with his condition; he was often moderately but never satisfactorily drunk. I never watched a man's condition with such absorbing interest.

At last, one evening, I hurried to his .cabin, for I learned that this time his situation was such that even the most fastidious could find no fault with it—he was tranquilly, serenely, symmetrically drunk—not a hiccup to mar his voice, not a cloud upon his brain thick enough to obscure his memory. As I entered, he was sitting upon an empty powder keg, with a clay pipe in one hand and the other raised to command silence. The boys said "Shhh—! Don't speak. He's going to commence."

"I don't reckon them times will ever come again. They never was a more bullier old ram than what he was.[35] Grandfather got that old ram from a feller up in Siskiyou County and fetched him home and turned him loose in the medder, and next morning he went down to have a look at him, and accident'ly dropped a ten-cent piece in the grass and stooped down—so—and was a-fumblin' around in the grass to git it, and the ram he was a-standin' up the slope taking notice; but my grandfather wasn't taking notice, because he had his back to the ram and was int-rested about the dime. Well, there he was, as I was a-sayin', down at the foot of the slope a-bendin' over—so—fumblin' in the grass, and the ram he was up there at the top of the slope, and Smith—Smith was a-standin' there —no, not jest there, a little further away—fifteen foot perhaps —well, my grandfather was a-stoopin' way down—so—and the ram was up there observing, you know, and Smith he . . . the ram he bent his head down, so . . . Smith of Calaveras . . . no, no it couldn't ben Smith of Calaveras—I remember now that he—b'George it was Smith of Tulare County—course it was, I remember it now perfectly plain.

"Well, Smith he stood just there, and my grandfather he

stood just here, you know, and he was a-bendin' down just so, fumblin' in the grass, and when the old ram see him in that attitude he took it fur an invitation—and here he come! down the slope thirty mile an hour and his eye full of business. You see my grandfather's back being to him, and him stooping down like that, of course he—why sho! it *warn't* Smith of Tulare at all, it was Smith of Sacramento—my goodness, how did I ever come to get them Smiths mixed like that—why, Smith of Tulare was jest a nobody, but Smith of Sacramento —why the Smiths of Sacramento come of the best Southern blood in the United States; there warn't ever any better blood south of the line than the Sacramento Smiths. Why, look here, one of them married a Whitaker! I reckon that gives you an idea of the kind of society the Sacramento Smiths could 'sociate around in; there ain't no better blood than that Whitaker blood; I reckon anybody'll tell you that.

"Look at Mariar Whitaker—there was a girl for you! Little? Why, yes, she was little, but what of that? Look at the heart of her—had a heart like a bullock—just as good and sweet and lovely and generous as the day is long; if she had a thing and you wanted it, you could have it—have it and welcome; why Mariar Whitaker couldn't have a thing and another person need it and not get it—get it and welcome. She had a glass eye, and she used to lend it to Flora Ann Baxter that hadn't any, to receive company with; well, she was pretty large, and it didn't fit; it was a number seven, and she was excavated for a fourteen, and so that eye wouldn't lay still; every time she winked it would turn over. It was a beautiful eye and set her off admirable, because it was a lovely pale blue on the front side—the side you look out of—and it was gilded on the back side; didn't match the other eye, which was one of them brown yellery eyes and tranquil and quiet, you know, the way that kind of eyes are; but that warn't any matter—they worked together all right and plenty picturesque. When Flora Ann winked, that blue and gilt eye would whirl over, and the other one stand still, and as soon as she begun to get excited that hand-made eye would give a whirl and then go on a-whirlin' and a-whirlin' faster and faster, and a-flashin' first blue and then yaller and then blue and then yaller, and when it got to whizzing and flashing like that, the oldest man in the world couldn't keep up with the expression on that side of her face.[36] Grown people didn't mind it, but it most always made the children cry, it was sort o' scary.[37] Flora Ann Baxter married a Hogadorn. I reckon that lets you understand what kind of blood she was—old Maryland Eastern Shore blood; not a better family in the United States than the Hogadorns.

"Sally—that's Sally Hogadorn—Sally married a missionary, and they went off carrying the good news to the cannibals out in one of them way-off islands around the world in the middle of the ocean somers, and they et her; et him, too, which was irregular; it warn't the custom to eat the missionary, but only the family, and when they see what they had done they was dreadful sorry about it, and when the relations sent down there to fetch away the things they said so—said so right out —said they were sorry, and 'pologized, and said it shouldn't happen again; said 'twas an accident.

"Accident! Now that's foolishness; there ain't no such thing as an accident; there ain't nothing happens in the world but what's ordered just so by a wiser Power than us, and it's always fur a good purpose; we don't know what the good purpose was, sometimes—and it was the same with the families that was short a missionary and his wife. But that ain't no matter, and it ain't any of our business; all that concerns us is that it was a special providence and it had a good intention. No, sir, there ain't no such thing as an accident.

"Why, you look at my Uncle Lem—what do you say to that?

That's all I ask you—you just look at my Uncle Lem and talk
to me about accidents! One day my Uncle Lem and his dog
was downtown, and he was a-leanin' up against a scaffolding
—sick, or drunk, or somethin'—and there was an Irishman with
a hod of bricks up the ladder along about the third story, and
his foot slipped and down he come, bricks and all, and hit a
stranger fair and square and knocked the everlasting aspira-
tions out of him; he was ready for the coroner in two minutes.
Now then people said it was an accident.

"Accident! there warn't no accident about it; 'twas a special providence, and had a mysterious, noble intention back of
it. The idea was to save that Irishman. If the stranger hadn't
been there that Irishman would have been killed. The people
said 'special providence'—sho! the dog was there—why didn't
the Irishman fall on the dog? Why warn't the dog app'inted?
Fer a mighty good reason—the dog would 'a' seen him a-coming; you can't depend on no dog to carry out a special providence. You couldn't hit a dog with an Irishman because—
lemme see, what was that dog's name ... oh, yes, Jasper—and
a mighty good dog, too; he wa'n't no common dog, he wa'n't
no mongrel; he was a composite. A composite dog is a dog
that's made up of all the valuable qualities that's in the dog
breed—kind of a syndicate; and a mongrel is made up of the
riffraff that's left over. That Jasper was one of the most wonderful dogs you ever see. Uncle Lem got him of the Wheelers.
I reckon you've heard of the Wheelers; ain't no better blood
south of the line than the Wheelers.

"One day Wheeler was a-meditating and dreaming around
in the carpet factory and the machinery made a snatch at him
and first you know he was a-meandering all over that factory
from the garret to the cellar, and everywhere, at such another
gait as—why, you couldn't even see him; you could only hear
him whiz when he went by. Well, you know a person can't go

through an experience like that and arrive back home the way he was when he went. No, Wheeler got wove up into thirty-nine yards of the best three-ply carpeting. The widder was sorry, she was uncommon sorry, and loved him and done the best she could fur him in the circumstances, which was unusual. She took the whole piece—thirty-nine yards—and she wanted to give him proper and honorable burial, but she couldn't bear to roll him up; she took and spread him out full length, and said she wouldn't have it any other way. She wanted to buy a tunnel for him but there wasn't any tunnel for sale, so she boxed him in a beautiful box and stood it on the hill on a pedestal twenty-one foot high, and so it was a monument and grave together, and economical—sixty foot high—you could see it from everywhere—and she painted on it 'To the loving memory of thirty-nine yards of the best three-ply carpeting containing the mortal remainders of Millington G. Wheeler—go thou and do likewise.' "

At this point the historian's voice began to wobble and his eyelids to droop with weariness, and he fell asleep; and so from that day to this we are still in ignorance; we don't know whether the old grandfather ever got the ten-cent piece out of the grass; we haven't any idea what it was that happened, or whether anything happened at all.[38]

From time to time I had amused myself by writing letters to the *Territorial Enterprise* in Virginia City, the chief paper in the Territory. I was always surprised when they appeared in print and my good opinion of the editors steadily declined. Presently, an offer arrived to come up to Virginia and work for the *Enterprise* for $25.00 a week. I took it.[39]

I did not often meddle in politics. We had a political editor who was already excellent and needed only a term or two in the penitentiary to be perfect.[40] But, occasionally, I was sent down to Carson City to cover the insurrections in our Territorial legislature. This was during the time of the great silver boom and I think I can say, and say with pride, that we had a legislature which brought higher prices than any in the world. One of our most prominent men down there got a bill passed to pay for a ten thousand dollar agricultural fair to show off forty dollars' worth of pumpkins. Grown on his brother's farm. He showed promise in a political way and would have got a reputation and gone to Washington, if he had lived. He was shot by some friends of his over a small difference of opinion. I bore him no malice.[41] I would send him a fan if I could.[42] I did not attend his funeral; but I wrote a very nice letter saying that I approved of it.[43]

While I was there in Virginia City the great humorist Artemus Ward came for a lecture. I had heard of him but I had never seen him before. I was asked to have breakfast with him and get an interview. Now it was almost religion, there in the silver mines, to have some whiskey before breakfast, to wake up the blood and start it circulating. Artemus, with the true cosmopolitan instinct, always went along with the customs of the country he was in, so he had three. I said I would rather not have any; I was anxious to interview Artemus Ward and get all my facts straight, but he gently insisted and I drank it down, feeling that I was doing something I might be sorry for.

Artemus dropped an unimportant remark or two, and then assumed a look of superhuman earnestness, and made the following astounding speech:

"Now there is one thing I ought to ask you about before I forget it. You have been here in Silverland—here in Nevada —two or three years and, of course your position on the daily newspaper has made it necessary for you to go down in the mines and examine them carefully in detail, and therefore you know all about the silver-mining business. Now, what I want to get at is—is, well, the way the deposits of ore are made, you know. For instance. Now, as I understand it, the vein which contains the silver is sandwiched in between casings of granite, and runs along the ground, and sticks up like a curbstone. Well, take a vein forty feet thick, for example, or eighty, for that matter, or even a hundred—say you go down on it with a shaft, straight down, you know, or with what you call 'incline,' maybe you go down five hundred feet, or maybe you don't go down but two hundred—anyway you go down, and all the time this vein grows narrower, when the casings come nearer or approach each other, you may say— that is, when they do approach, which, of course, they don't always do, particularly in cases where the nature of the formation is such that they stand apart wider than they otherwise would, and which geology has failed to account for, although everything in that science goes to prove that, all things being equal, it would if it did not, or would not certainly if it did, and then, of course, they are. Don't you think it is?"

"I—I—that is—if you don't mind, would you—would you say that over again?"

"Oh, certainly, certainly! You see, I am very unfamiliar with the subject, and perhaps I don't present my case clearly . . ."

"No, no—no, no—you state it plain enough, but that whiskey has muddled me a little. No, I do understand you, but I would get the hang of it better if you went over it again. I'll pay better attention this time."

"What I was after was this. This vein, or lode, or ledge, or whatever you call it, runs along between two layers of granite, just the same as if it were a sandwich. Very well. Now suppose you go down on that—say a thousand feet, or maybe twelve hundred, it don't really matter—before you drift; and then you start your drifts, some of them across the ledge and others along the length of it, where the sulphurets—I believe they call them sulphurets; though why they should, considering that so far as I can see the main dependence of a miner does not so lie, as some suppose, but in which it cannot be successfully maintained, in which the same should not continue, while part and parcel of the same ore—not committed to either in the sense referred to—whereas under different circumstances the most inexperienced among us could not detect it, if it were, or might overlook it, if it did, or scorn the whole idea of such a thing, even though it were demonstrated as such. Am I right?"

"I feel ashamed of myself, Mr. Ward. I know I ought to understand you, perfectly well, but the whiskey has got into my head, and now I can't understand even the simplest proposition. I told you how it would be."

"Oh, don't mind it, don't mind it; it's my own fault, no doubt—though I did think it clear enough for . . ."

"Clear! Why, listen, you stated it as clear as the sun to anybody but an abject idiot; but it's that confounded whiskey that's played all the mischief."

"No, now don't say that. I'll begin it all over again . . ."

"No, don't—don't do anything of the kind, please, because I tell you my head is in such a condition that I don't believe I could understand the most trifling question a man could ask me."

"Now don't you be afraid. I'll put it so plain this time that you can't help but get the hang of it. We'll begin at the very beginning."

I made up my mind I'd understand him this time or turn myself in to the asylum.

"You know the vein, the ledge, the thing that contains the

metal, whereby it constitutes the medium between all other forces, whether of present or remote agencies, so brought to bear in favor of the former against the latter, or the latter against the former or all, or both, or comprising the relative differences existing within the radium whence culminate the several degress of similarity to which . . ."

"Oh, hang my wooden head, it ain't any use!—it ain't any use to try—I can't understand anything. The plainer you get it the more I can't get the hang of it."

By noon I had heard that story nine or ten more times and had I don't know how many drinks and was on the edge of delirium tremens. They put me to bed, with a wet rag around my head; and it seemed to me that as Artemus closed the door I heard him sobbing, but I couldn't be sure. I never touched liquor for three days. Then I found I'd been sold.

Artemus Ward was one of the best fellows in the world, and one of the most companionable. It's been said that he was not fluent in conversation, but I differ.[44]

Occasionally I went over to San Francisco on a holiday. On one of those trips I arrived with a very bad cold. A lady at the hotel advised me to drink a quart of whiskey every twenty-four hours, and another friend recommended exactly the same thing. That made half a gallon. I did. The cold died, and I still live.[45]

It was not exactly a holiday. I had to send back a story or two to the *Enterprise* in Virginia City, so on one occasion I covered "The Pioneer Ball," a fashionable event of the season. I knew that the feminine fashions displayed at this ball would be of interest to my society friends in the mining camps. I knew they would be pining to hear about this glittering jamboree, so I wrote of the ensemble worn by Mrs. Sandy Baldwin, which was particularly noteworthy. "She was arrayed in a sorrel organdy, trimmed with fustians and figaros, and canzou fichus, so disposed as to give a splendid effect without disturbing the general harmony of the dress. The body of the robe was a zero velvet, goffered with a square pelerine of solferino *poil de chevere* amidships. The fan used by Mrs. B. was of real palm-leaf and cost $4,000—the handle alone cost six bits. Her headdress was composed of a graceful cataract of white chantilly lace surmounted by a few artificial worms, and butterflies and things, and a tasteful tarantula done in jet. It is impossible to conceive of anything more enchanting than this toilet—or the lady who wore it, either, for that matter.

"Mrs. J. B. Winters was dressed in a rich white satin, with a body composed of a gorgeously figured mackinaw blanket, with five rows of ornamental brass buttons down the back. The dress was looped up at the side with several bows of No. 3 ribbon-yellow—displaying a skirt of cream-colored valenciennes crocheted with pink crewel. The coiffure was simply a tall cone of brilliant field-flowers, upon the summit of which stood glittering 'golden beetle'—or, as we call him at home, a 'straddle-bug.' From the top of her head depended tasteful garlands of fresh radishes. All who saw the beautiful Mrs. W. upon this occasion will agree that there was nothing wanting about her dress to make it attract attention in any community." [46]

I eventually left Virginia City and went to San Francisco, where I became unemployed. A pawnbroker took care of what property I had. In those days I used to meet an old lady on the street every day or so, and one day she stopped me and said, "Mr. Clemens, I'm worried about you. I see you marching up and down this street every day with a cigar box under your arm. I am afraid you're smoking too much." I said, "No, ma'am, I'm just moving again."

I had this friend who was a poet. He was also out of a job and things were going very bad with him. My friend the poet said he thought his life was a failure. I said I thought it was, too. Then he said he wanted to commit suicide. I said "all right"—which was disinterested advice to a friend in trouble. But like all such advice there was just the least bit of self-interest behind it. I knew that if I could get a "scoop" on the other newspapers I could get a job.

It was necessary to keep this thing fresh in my friend's mind. Would-be suicides are very changeable and hard to hold to their purpose. Especially poets. He had a preference for a pistol, which was extravagant. We hadn't enough between us to hire a pistol. A fork would have been easier.

But he finally decided to drown himself and I said that was an excellent idea—the only trouble being he was such a good swimmer. But we went down to the beach anyway. I went along, too, to see the thing was done right. And then something most romantic happened. There came in on that sea something that had been on its way for years. It rolled in across that broad Pacific with a message that was full of meaning for that poor poet. It was a life preserver!

Here was a complication. But then I had an idea—he never had any, especially when he was going to write poetry; I suggested that we pawn the life preserver and get a revolver. The pawnbroker gave us an old derringer with a bullet as big as a hickory nut. When he found it was only a poet who was going to kill himself, he didn't even quibble about the price. It was a terrible moment when my friend placed that pistol against his forehead and stood for an instant, waiting. Then I said, "Oh, pull the trigger!" And he did, and the bullet cleaned out all the grey matter in his brains. It also carried away the poetic faculty and now that fellow's a useful member of society again.⁴⁷

By and by, an old friend of mine, a miner, came down from one of the decayed mining camps of Tuolumne, California, and I went back with him. We lived in a small cabin on Jackass Hill—it was so named before I got there, there is no connection—and we employed ourselves with what is called "pocket mining." Here, the gold is not evenly distributed through the surface dirt, as in ordinary placer mines, but is collected in little spots, and they are very wide apart and hard to find; but when you do find one you reap a rich and sudden harvest. I have known one of those pocket miners to hunt patiently about the hillsides every day for eight months without finding gold enough to make a snuff-box—his grocery bill running up relentlessly all the time—and then find a pocket and take out of it two thousand dollars in two dips of his shovel. I have known him to take out three thousand dollars in two hours and go and pay up every cent of his indebtedness, then enter on a dazzling spree that finished the last of his treasure before the night was gone. And the next day he bought his groceries on credit, as usual, and shouldered his pan and shovel and went off to the hills hunting pockets again, happy and content. This is the most fascinating of all the different kinds of mining, and furnishes a very handsome percentage of victims to the lunatic asylum.

One of my comrades there—a victim of eighteen years of unrequited toil and blighted hopes—was one of the gentlest spirits that ever bore its patient cross in a weary exile: grave and simple Jim Baker, whose story of the bluejays I incorporated in *A Tramp Abroad*.

We prospected for some time around Angel's Camp, in Calaveras County, and it was in the saloon there that I heard old Simon Wheeler relate his story of the Jumping Frog.⁴⁸

I found Simon Wheeler dozing comfortably by the bar-room stove of the dilapidated tavern in the decayed mining camp of Angel's, and I told him that a friend of mine had asked me to make some inquiries about a cherished companion of his boyhood named *Leonidas W.* Smiley—*Rev. Leonidas W. Smiley*, a young minister of the Gospel, who he had heard was at one time a resident of Angel's Camp.

Simon Wheeler backed me into a corner and blockaded me there with his chair, and then sat down and reeled off the monotonous narrative which follows. He never smiled, he never frowned, he never changed his voice from the gentle-flowing key to which he tuned his initial sentence, he never betrayed the slightest suspicion of enthusiasm; but all through the interminable narrative there ran a vein of impressive earnestness and sincerity, which showed me plainly that, so far from his imagining that there was anything ridiculous or funny about his story, he regarded it as a really important matter, and admired its two heroes as men of transcendent genius in *finesse*.

"Rev. Leonidas W., H'm, Reverend Le—well, there was a feller here once by the name of *Jim* Smiley, in the winter of '49—or maybe it was the spring of '50—I don't recollect exactly, somehow, though what makes me think it was one or the other is because I remember the big flume warn't finished when he first come to the camp; but anyway, he was the curiousest man about always betting on anything that turned up you ever see, if he could get anybody to bet on the other side; and if he couldn't he'd change sides. Anyway what suited the other man would suit *him*—just so's he got a bet, *he* was satisfied. And he was lucky, uncommon lucky; he most always come out winner. There couldn't be no solit'ry thing mentioned but that feller'd offer to bet on it. If there was a dog-fight, he'd bet on it; if there was a cat-fight, he'd

bet on it; why, if there was two birds setting on a fence, he
would bet you which one would fly first. If he even see a
straddle-bug start to go anywheres, he would bet you how
long it would take him to get to—to wherever he was going
to, and if you took him up, he would foller that straddle-bug
to Mexico but what he would find out where he was bound
for and how long he was on the road. He'd bet on *anything*—
the dangdest feller. Parson Walker's wife laid very sick once,
for a good while, and it seemed as if they warn't going to
save her; but one morning he come in, and Smiley up and
asked him how she was, and he said she was considerable
better—thank the Lord for his inf'nite mercy—and coming on
so smart that with the blessing of Prov'dence she'd get well
yet; and Smiley, before he thought, says, 'Well, I'll risk two-
and-a-half she don't anyway.'

"Well, thish-yer Smiley he ketched a frog one day, and
took him home, and said he cal'lated to educate him; and so
he never done nothing for three months but set in his back
yard and learn that frog to jump. And you bet you he *did*
learn him, too. He'd give him a little punch behind, and the
next minute you'd see that frog whirling in the air like a
doughnut—see him turn one summer-set, or maybe a couple,
if he got a good start, and come down flat-footed and all
right, like a cat. He got him up so in the matter of ketching
flies. Why, I've seen him set Dan'l Webster down here on this
floor—Dan'l Webster was the name of the frog—and sing out,
'Flies, Dan'l, flies!' and quicker'n you could wink he'd spring
straight up and snake a fly off'n the counter there, and flop
down on the floor ag'in as solid as a gob of mud, and fall to
scratching the side of his head with his hind foot as indifferent as if he hadn't no idea he'd been doin' any more'n any
frog might do. You never see a frog so modest and straight-
for'ard as he was, for all he was so gifted. And when it come

to fair and square jumping on a dead level, he could get over more ground at one straddle than any animal of his breed you ever see. Jumping on a dead level was his strong suit, you understand; and when it come to that, Smiley would ante up money on him as long as he had a red.

"Well, Smiley kep' the beast in a little lattice box, and he used to fetch him downtown sometimes and lay for a bet. One day a feller—a stranger in the camp, he was—come acrost him with his box, and says:

" 'What might it be that you've got in the box?'

"And Smiley says, sorter indifferent-like, 'It might be a parrot, or it might be a canary, maybe, but it ain't—it's only just a frog.'

"And the feller took it, and looked at it careful, and turned it round this way and that, and says, 'H'm—so 'tis. Well, what's *he* good for?'

" 'Well,' Smiley says, easy and careless, 'he's good enough for *one* thing, I should judge—he can outjump any frog in Calaveras County.'

"The feller took the box again, and took another long, particular look, and give it back to Smiley, and says, very deliberate, 'Well,' he says, 'I don't see no p'ints about that frog that's any better'n any other frog.'

" 'Maybe you don't,' Smiley says. 'Maybe you understand frogs and maybe you don't understand 'em; maybe you've had experience, and maybe you ain't only a amature, as it were. Anyways, I've got *my* opinion, and I'll resk forty dollars that he can outjump any frog in Calaveras County.'

"And the feller studied a minute, and then says, kinder sad-like, 'Well, I'm only a stranger here, and I ain't got no frog; but if I had a frog, I'd bet you.'

"And then Smiley says, 'That's all right—that's all right—if you'll hold my box a minute, I'll go and get you a frog.'

And so the feller took the box, and put up his forty dollars along with Smiley's, and set down to wait.

"So he set there a good while thinking and thinking to himself, and then he got the frog out and prized his mouth open and took a teaspoon and filled him full of quail-shot—filled him pretty near up to his chin—and set him on the floor. Smiley he went to the swamp and slopped around in the mud for a long time, and finally he ketched a frog, and fetched him in, and give him to this feller, and says:

" 'Now, if you're ready, set him alongside of Dan'l, with his fore paws just even with Dan'l's, and I'll give the word.' Then he says, 'One—two—three—*git!*' and him and the feller touched up the frogs from behind, and the new frog hopped off lively, but Dan'l give a heave, and hysted up his shoulders —so—like a Frenchman, but it warn't no use—he couldn't budge; he was planted as solid as a church, and he couldn't no more stir than if he was anchored out. Smiley was a good deal surprised, and he was disgusted too, but he didn't have no idea what the matter was, of course.

"The feller took the money and started away; and when he was going out at the door, he sorter jerked his thumb over his shoulder—so—at Dan'l, and says again, very deliberate, 'Well,' he says, '*I* don't see no p'ints about that frog that's any better'n any other frog.'

"Smiley he stood scratching his head and looking down at Dan'l a long time, and at last he says, 'I do wonder what in the nation that frog throw'd off for—I wonder if there ain't something the matter with him—he 'pears to look mighty baggy, somehow.' And he ketched Dan'l by the nap of the neck, and hefted him, and says, 'Why blame my cats if he don't weigh five pound!' and turned him upside down and he belched out a double handful of shot. And then he see how it was, and he was the maddest man—he set the frog down and took out after that feller, but he never ketched him. And—thish-yer Smiley had a yaller one-eyed cow that didn't have no tail, only just a short stump like a bannanner, and—"

However, lacking both time and inclination, I did not wait to hear about the afflicted cow, but took my leave.[49]

My mining reminiscences prompt me to call to your attention the recent news dispatch from San Francisco, entitled "Gold in Solution" in the Calostoga Springs. It says that the proprietor of the Springs has extracted $1,000 in gold of the utmost fineness from ten barrels of water during a fortnight by a process known only to himself. This will surprise many people, but it does not surprise me, for I once owned those Springs myself. What does surprise me, however, is the falling off in the richness of the water. In my time the yield was a dollar a dipperful. I am not saying this to injure the property, in case a sale is contemplated; I am only saying it in the interest of history.

It may be that this hotel proprietor's process is an inferior one—yes, that may be the fault. Mine was to take my uncle —I had an extra uncle at the time—and fill him up, and let him stand fifteen minutes to give the water a chance to settle well, then insert him in an exhausted receiver, which had the effect of sucking the gold out through his pores. I have taken more than eleven thousand dollars out of that old man in a day and a half.[50]

Presently, I found myself in San Francisco again, without a cent. Then Lady Luck finally smiled on me and I was given

a berth on the *Sacramento Union,* as their special correspondent to the Sandwich Islands.

Our first stop was Honolulu. I was naturally anxious to
fully explore this dreamy, enchanted place, and they told me
the best way to do so was to hire a horse. I'd had some un-
pleasant experiences with these unpredictable creatures before. In Carson City I'd once made the mistake of buying
a Genuine Mexican Plug—on the advice of a man I later
found out was the auctioneer's brother. As soon as I mounted
that horse he put all his feet together in a bunch, lowered his
back, and shot me straight into the air about three or four
feet. I came down on the horse's neck, shot up again, came
down almost on the high pommel [51]—which was too much
variety for me.[52] I decided to get off; but I was in the air
again before I could find out which way to go. While I was
up that time somebody sings out, *"Don't* he buck, though!"
Then a stranger struck the horse with a leather strap, and
when I arrived down again the Genuine Mexican Plug was
not there. I dug myself out of the ground and made up my
mind that if the auctioneer's brother's funeral took place
while I was in Carson City I would postpone all other recrea-
tions and attend it.

So in Honolulu I said I preferred a safe horse to a fast one.
I asked for an excessively gentle horse—one with no spirit
whatsoever. A lame one, if they had such a thing.[53] They
showed me an animal who looked as if he wanted to lean up
against something and think; [54] so I chose him. I could see
he had as many fine points as any other horse, so I hung my
hat on one of them, behind the saddle, and started off.

The first gate he came to we started in. I argued the case
with him and he resisted, but ultimately yielded to insult and
abuse. He backed out of that gate and steered for another
one on the other side of the street.

Well, he finally abandoned the gate business and went along peaceably enough, but absorbed in meditation. This began to worry me. I said to myself, this horse is planning some outrage; no horse ever thought over a subject as profoundly as this one is doing just for nothing. The more the thing preyed on my mind, the more uneasy I got. Finally I dismounted to see if there was anything wild in his eye. I can't tell you what a relief it was to find he was only asleep. I woke him up and that startled him into a convulsive canter which had three short steps in it and one long one, something like the sweeping plunge of a ship in a storm.

The saddle was an American saddle, with no seat to it to speak of—one might as well sit in a shovel. And the stirrups are nothing but an ornamental nuisance. Sometimes I got one foot so far through it took on the nature of an anklet; sometimes both feet were through and I was handcuffed by the legs. Even when I was in proper position and carefully balanced on the balls of my feet—oh, well, the subject is too exasperating to talk about.

About noon, I whipped my animated trance alongside a stretch of sandy beach where I had noticed a bevy of nude young native ladies bathing in the sea. This was the sort of local color I was after for my newspaper, so I went down and sat on their clothes, to keep them from being stolen, and begged them to come out for it seemed to me the sea was rising—I was satisfied they were running some risk. But they went right on with their sport, swimming races, splashing and tumbling each other about, enjoying themselves tremendously. I stayed there for some time, for I intended to be conscientious about my report to the newspaper. I finally turned round to leave and the horse was asleep again. It was singular. It proves that there is some difference between the

horse and the man, after all. You cannot rely on a horse to
gather news.

When the missionaries first came to Honolulu, those native
women called on them to pay their respects, not even clothed
with a blush. This put a strain on decorum. But in church,
faced with a completely naked congregation, the poor
preacher found it difficult to keep to the text and go on with
the services. Here was a serious problem in morale which
had been generally skipped over in divinity school and at
first the missionaries were nonplussed.[55]

But then they remembered the Christian principle that
nothing needs reforming so much as other people's habits,[56]
and that solved the problem. They pointed out to their con-
verts that it's hard enough to get into heaven fully clothed.
But to attempt it naked might seem like blasphemy. Then
they imported a quantity of hats, bonnets, and other wearing
apparel, distributed them, and begged these descendents of
Adam and Eve not to come to church naked next Sunday, as
usual. And they didn't. But, being an unselfish people, the
natives divided up with their neighbors and on the following Sabbath, in the midst of the reading of a hymn, a stately
brown dame would sweep up the aisle with nothing in the
world on but a stove-pipe hat and a pair of cheap gloves.
Another would enter, with a flourish, with just the sleeves of
a bright calico dress tied round her waist and the rest of the
garment dragging behind, like a peacock's tail off duty. A
stately buck would enter with the legs of a pair of pantaloons
tied around his neck, and the rest of his person untram-
meled.

The poor creatures were beaming with complacency and
perfectly satisfied that they were as well dressed for the hereafter as any other Christian. They gazed at each other with

a good deal of admiration, and it was plain to see that the young girls were taking note of what each other had on, just as if they'd always lived in a land of Bibles and knew what churches were made for. Here was the evidence of a dawning civilization.

Under the circumstances, there wasn't anything for the missionaries to do but throw in the sponge and cut the whole thing short with the benediction.

Well, the coming of civilization has made a great change in those lovely islands. The natives all wear clothes now for the protection of tourists, as well as missionaries. And all that church-going has finally built up in the native women a profound respect for chastity—in other people.

In fact, many of the old customs have died out altogether. I visited one ancient temple where human sacrifices used to be offered up. In the good old days when a native yielded to sin, he acknowledged it by coming forward, with noble frankness, and offering up his grandmother as an atonement. In those days a man could go on cleansing his conscience as long as his relations held out. But then the missionaries came and braved a thousand privations to tell them what a beautiful place heaven is and how nearly impossible it is to get there, and tell them what a dreary place hell is, and how easy it is to go there. And show them what rapture it is to work all day long, for fifty cents, to buy food for the next day, as compared with fishing and lolling in the sun through eternal summer and eating the food that nobody bothered to provide but Nature.

How sad it is to think of the multitudes who went to their graves on that beautiful island, and never knew there was a hell.[57]

I interviewed the King of the Sandwich Islands. He said,

"We understand Christianity. We have eaten the mission-aries." [58]

When I got back to San Francisco I found myself out of a job—so I hired a hall and gave a lecture. I've never had to do a day's work since. I had a new career. I went forth upon the public highway, with all the other bandits, and gave readings from my works. I made the acquaintance of that constant menace to the itinerant lecturer, the local interviewer. It is petrified custom with these people to probe you with personal questions which you try to answer as conscientiously as you can; then they run home and improve you. The result is that you do not recognize yourself in print, unless you happen to be an idiot of long standing, with no prejudices about it.

For years I have tried to outwit these people. One of those villains came to me one day, when I was out on a raid. He knocked on my hotel room door and announced that he was connected with the *Daily Thunderstorm*. I was going to break the chair over him, but he sat down on it before I could go into action.[59] I was not at my best that morning. My powers were somewhat under a cloud. So I decided that I had better try to confuse him.

He started it off. He said, "You know it is the custom, now, to interview any man who has become notorious."

"What do you do it with?"

"Ah, well, customarily it consists in the interviewer asking questions and the interviewed answering them. It is all the rage now. Will you let me ask you certain questions calculated to bring out the salient points of your public and private life?"

"I have a very bad memory..."

"Oh, that's all right. Just so you will try to do the best you can."

"I will. I will put my whole mind to it."

"Thanks. Now. Are you ready to begin?"

"Ready."

"How old are you?"

"Nineteen, in June."

"Well—I would have taken you to be much older than that."

"Thank you very much."

"Where were you born?"

"In Missouri."

"When did you first begin to write?"

"In 1836."

"Why, how could that be, if you are only nineteen now?"

"I don't know. That does strike you as curious, somehow, doesn't it?"

"Yes. Whom do you consider the most remarkable man you ever met?"

"Aaron Burr."

"Aaron Burr! But you never could have met Aaron Burr if you are only nineteen years—"

"Now, if you know more about me than I do, what do you ask me for?"

"Well ... it was only a suggestion. How did you happen to meet Burr?"

"I happened to be at his funeral one day, and he asked me to make less noise ..."

"Good heavens! If you were at his funeral, he must have been dead; and if he was dead, how could he care whether you made a noise or not?"

"Oh, he was always a particular kind of a man that way."

"Now let me get this straight: you say he spoke to you, and yet he was *dead*."

"I didn't say he was dead."

"But . . . wasn't he?"

"Some said he was, some said he wasn't."

"What did you think?"

"It was none of my business. It wasn't my funeral."

"Well, let's drop that. Let me ask about something else. Have you any brothers or sisters?"

"I—I—I—think so—yes—but I don't remember."

"Well, that is the most extraordinary statement I ever heard! I'm sure you had a brother. Haven't I read that somewhere?"

"Oh. Yes, now that you mention it; there was a brother William—*Bill* we called him. Poor old Bill!"

"Why? Is he dead?"

"We never could tell. There was a great mystery about that, you see."

"That is sad. He disappeared, then?"

"Well, yes, in a sort of general way. We buried him."

"*Buried* him! Without knowing whether he was dead or not?"

"Oh, no. He was dead enough, all right. You see, we were twins—defunct and I—and we got mixed in the bathtub when we were only two weeks old, and one of us was drowned. But we didn't know which. Some think it was Bill. Some think it was me."

"What do you think?"

"I would give worlds to know. This solemn, this awful mystery has cast a gloom over my whole life. But I'll tell you a secret which I've never revealed to anyone before. One of

us had a peculiar mark—a large mole on the back of his left hand; that was *me*. That child was the one that was drowned."
Then the young man withdrew.[60]

After my adventures out there on the Pacific Coast I came east, and joined an excursion to the Holy Land. Everybody was going that year. It was a kind of picnic on a gigantic scale.[61]

Now, in this place, let me bring you a selection from one of the world's great books on travel: *The Innocents Abroad* by Samuel Clemens.

You know, I am always sorry to have my name mentioned as one of the great authors because they have such a sad habit of dying off. Chaucer is dead. Spencer is dead. So is Milton, and so is Shakespeare. And I am not feeling very well myself.[62]

Those of you who have travelled abroad will recall, I'm sure, those necessary nuisances, European guides. All their lives they are employed in showing strange things to foreigners, and listening to their bursts of admiration. It is human nature to take delight in exciting admiration. That is what makes gossips turn out in rain and storm to go and be the first to tell a startling bit of news. Think, then, what a passion it becomes with a guide, whose privilege it is, every day, to show strangers wonders that throw them into ecstasies of admiration! He gets so that he could not live in a soberer atmosphere. Once we discovered this, we never went into ecstasies any more—never showed anything but impassive faces and stupid indifference in the presence of the sublimest wonders a guide had to display. We made some of those people savage, at times, but we never lost our own serenity.

Now the guides in Genoa are delighted to secure an American party, because Americans deal so much in sentiment and emotion before any relic of Columbus. Our guide there fidgeted about as if he'd swallowed a spring mattress.

"Come with me, gentlemen!—come!—I show you the letter writing by Christopher Colombo.—Write it himself!—Write with his own hand!—Come!"

The doctor asked the questions, generally, because he can look more like an inspired idiot and throw more imbecility into the tone of his voice than any man who lives. It comes natural to him. So the doctor examined the stained and aged document very deliberately, during a painful pause.

"What did you say was the name of the party who wrote this?"

"Christopher Colombo! The great Christopher Colombo."

"Did he write it himself—or how?"

"He write it himself. Christopher Colombo! His own handwriting; write by himself!"

"Why, I have seen boys in America only fourteen years old who could write better than that."

"But this is the great . . ."

"I don't care *who* it is! It's the worst handwriting I ever saw. If you've got any specimens of penmanship of real merit, trot them out—and if you haven't, drive on."

We drove on. The guide was considerably shaken up, but he made another venture. He said he had something he thought would overcome us.

"Ah, gentlemen, you come with me! I show you the beautiful, O, magnificent bust Christopher Colombo. Splendid, grand, magnificent!"

He brought us before the beautiful bust, for it was beautiful, and sprang back and struck an attitude.

"Ah, gentlemen. See! Beautiful, grand bust Christopher Colombo. Beautiful bust, beautiful pedestal!"

The doctor examined the bust.

"Ferguson"—that was the name we had given our guide—
"Ferguson, what did I understand you to say this gentleman's
name was?"

"Christopher Colombo, the great Christopher Colombo!"

"What did he do?"

"He discover America!"

"Discover America? Oh, no, no, that statement will hardly
wash. We are just from America ourselves. We heard nothing
about it. Christopher Colombo—pleasant name. Is he dead?"

"Santa Maria! Three hundred years!"

"What did he die of?"

"I do not know. I cannot tell."

"Measles, you think?"

"Maybe, maybe. I think he die of something."

"Parents living?"

"Impossible!"

"Which is the bust here, and which is the pedestal?"

"Corpo di Baccho! *This* is the bust! *This* is the pedestal."

"Oh, I see. Yes. Happy combination. Very happy combination, indeed. Tell me, is this the first time this gentleman
was ever on a bust?"

He had reserved what he considered to be his greatest
wonder to the last—a royal Egyptian mummy. The best pre-
served in the world, perhaps. He felt so sure, this time, that
some of his old enthusiasm came back to him.

"Gentlemen—see! Mummy. Mummy."

"Ferguson . . . what'd you say this chap's name was?"

"Name? He got no name. He's a mummy!"

"Born here, was he?"

"No, no. 'Gyptian mummy."

"Oh, Frenchman, I presume."

"No—no, not Frenchman! Not Roman! Born in Egypta!"

"Born in Egypta. Never heard of Egypta before. Mummy. Mummy. How calm he is. How self-possessed. Is he dead?"

That conquered him. Our Roman Ferguson was the most patient, long-suffering subject we had. We hated to part with him. We enjoyed his society very much. We trust he enjoyed ours, but we were harassed with doubts.[63]

I am not much impressed by museums any more. I was once shown two skulls of Christopher Columbus. One when he was a boy, and one when he was a man.[64]

On my pilgrimage to the Holy Land, I had made the acquaintance of a young man named Charley Langdon. He showed me an ivory miniature of his sister one day, and I promptly fell in love with her.

I saw her in the flesh for the first time the following December. She was slender and beautiful and girlish—she was both girl and woman. Two years later we were married.

It sounds easy and swift and unobstructed but that was not the way of it. It did not happen in that smooth and comfortable way. There was a good deal of courtship. There were three or four proposals and just as many refusals. I was roving far and wide on the lecture beat, but I managed to arrive in Elmira every now and then and renew the siege.

Once I dug an invitation out of Charley Langdon to come and stay a week. It was a pleasant week but it had to come to an end. But just at the last minute help and good fortune came from a most unexpected quarter. It was one of those cases so frequent in the past centuries, and so infrequent in our day—a case where the hand of Providence is in it.

I was ready to leave for New York. I bade goodbye to the family and Charley and I climbed into the wagon. We got in the back seat, which—fortunately for me—had not been fastened in its place. Barney, the coachman, touched up the horse with the whip, he made a sudden spring forward, and Charley and I went over the stern of the wagon backward. I struck exactly on the top of my head. I stood up that way for a moment, then crumbled down to the earth unconscious. It was a very good unconsciousness for a person who had not rehearsed the part. Nothing was the matter with me at all, but Charley was considerably battered. Yet he was so anxious about me he forgot about it. The family swarmed out, and poured enough brandy between my lips to strangle me and make me bark, but it did not diminish my unconsciousness— I was taking care of that myself.

They lugged me into the house and I recognized that this was a victory. I was there—the hand of Providence was in it!

They brought a bottle of some kind of liquid fire whose function was to reduce contusions. I knew that mine would scoff at it.

Livy's sister poured this on my head and pawed it around with her hand, stroking and massaging, until she got worn out; then Livy carried on for awhile. That was very pleasant. If Livy's manipulations had continued I should probably be unconscious to this day. It was very delightful, those manipulations. They soothed the fire right out of that "pain-killer."

I got three days extension out of that adventure and it helped a good deal. We became engaged, conditionally. But first, I needed references. I was an almost entirely unknown person, from the other side of the continent, and only those people out on the Pacific Coast would be able to furnish me with a character, in case I had one.

Mr. Langdon asked me for references. I furnished them and we waited. In due course, the answers came and I was sent for. The results were not promising. All those men were frank, to a fault; they not only spoke in disapproval of me,

they were enthusiastic about it. One of the clergymen proph-
esied that I would fill a drunkard's grave. It was just one of
those long-distance prophesies. There being no time limit,
there's no telling how long you may have to wait. So far—
well . . .

When Livy's father finished reading those letters there was
a good deal of a pause. It consisted largely of sadness and
solemnity. I couldn't think of anything to say. Mr. Langdon
was apparently in the same condition.

Finally he said:

"What kind of people are these? Haven't you a friend in
the world?"

"Apparently not."

"Then I'll be your friend. I know you better than they do.
Take the girl."

The engagement ring was plain and of heavy gold, engraved with the date February 4, 1869. A year later I took it
from her finger and prepared it to do service as a wedding
ring by having the wedding date engraved inside—February
2, 1870. It was never again removed from her finger, even for
a moment.

In Italy when death had restored her vanished youth to
her sweet face and she lay fair and beautiful and looking as
she had looked when she was a girl and a bride, they were
going to take that ring from her finger to keep for the children. But I prevented that sacrilege. It is buried with her.[65]

Shortly after my return from that excursion to the Holy
Land, I went to Washington. I was filled with a youthful zeal
to serve the country in some official capacity, so I got myself
appointed Clerk of the Senate Committee (their mistake) on
Conchology. I served for six days and then I resigned. I

could see plainly that the other members of the Government were determined to keep me from having any voice in the counsels of the nation, and I could no longer hold office and retain my self-respect.

To begin with, they appointed me clerk of that Committee on Conchology and then allowed me no one to play billiards with. I would have borne that, lonesome as it was, if I had met with courtesy from the other members of the Cabinet; but every time I went to one of them, when I saw they were doing something wrong, I was never even thanked for it. I went with the best intentions in the world to the Secretary of the Navy; I said:

"Sir, I cannot see that Admiral Farragut is doing anything but skirmishing around there in Europe, having a sort of a picnic. If there is no fighting for him to do, let him come home. There's no use in a man having a whole fleet for a pleasure excursion. It's too expensive. Mind, I do not object to pleasure excursions for the naval officers—if they are within reason; and economical. Let him go down the Mississippi on a raft. . . ."

You ought to have heard him storm! One would have thought I'd committed a crime of some kind. I said a raft was cheap, and full of republican simplicity, and perfectly safe. I said that for a tranquil pleasure excursion there was nothing equal to a raft.

He ordered me to leave the premises. My first impulse was to get him removed, but I let him stay.

I went next to the Secretary of the Treasury, who was not inclined to see me at all until he learned that I was connected with the Government. He said:

"What will *you* have?"

I asked him for a cigar, and a light; then began earnestly to point out to him the extravagant length of his annual report. I said it was expensive, unnecessary, and awkwardly constructed; there were no descriptive passages in it, no poetry, no sentiment—no plot nor pictures—not even wood-cuts. Nobody would read it, that was a clear case. I urged him not to ruin his reputation by getting out a thing like that. If he ever hoped to succeed in literature, he must throw more variety into his writing. I told him the main popularity of the almanac was derived from its poetry and conundrums, and that a few conundrums distributed around through his Treasury report would help the sale of it more than all the internal revenue he could put into it.

The Secretary of the Treasury fell into a violent passion. He said I was an ass. He abused me in the most vindictive manner, and said that if I came there again meddling with his business, he would throw me out of the window. It was just like a new author. They always think they know more than anybody else when they are getting out their first book. Nobody can tell *them* anything.

During the whole time that I was connected with the Government it seemed as if I could not do anything without getting myself into trouble. I never attended but one Cabinet meeting, but that was sufficient for me. The servant at the White House door did not even seem disposed to make way for me until I asked him if the other members of the Cabinet had arrived. They were all there. The President said:

"Well, sir, who are you?"

I handed him my card, and he read: "The Hon. Mark Twain, Clerk of the Senate Committee on Conchology." Then he looked at me from head to foot, as if he'd never heard of me before. The Secretary of the Treasury said:

"This is the meddlesome ass that came and told me to put poetry and conundrums into my report, as if it were an almanac."

The Secretary of the Navy said:

"I recognize this youth as the person who came to me with some insane proposal for sending Admiral Farragut down the Mississippi on a raft; for a pleasure excursion, as he put it."

I said:

"Gentlemen, I perceive here a disposition to debar me from all voice in the councils of the nation. No notice whatever was sent to me today. It was only by the merest chance that I learned there was going to be a Cabinet meeting. All I wish to know is, *is* this a Cabinet meeting, or is it not?"

The President said it was.

"Very well," I said, "let us proceed to business and not fritter away valuable time."

The Secretary of State now spoke up, in his benign way, and said:

"Young man, you are laboring under a mistake. The clerks of the Congressional committees are not members of the Cabinet. Therefore, much as we could desire your more than human wisdom in our deliberations, we cannot lawfully avail ourselves of it. The councils of the nation must proceed without you. If disaster follows, as follow full well it may, be assured that by deed and voice you did your best to avert it. You have my blessing. Farewell."

Well, these gentle words soothed me and I went away. But the servants of the nation can know no peace. I had hardly reached my den in the Capitol and put my feet on the table like a representative, when one of the Senators on the Conchological Committee came in, in a passion, and said:

"Where have you been all day?"

I said I had been to a Cabinet meeting.

"To a Cabinet meeting! I would like to know what business you had at a Cabinet meeting?"

I said I went there to consult. He grew insolent then and

said that he had been looking for me for three days to copy a report on bomb-shells, egg-shells, clam-shells and I don't know what all, connected with conchology, and nobody had been able to find me.

This was too much. I said:

"Sir, do you suppose I am going to *work* for six dollars a day? I am a slave of *no* faction. Take back your degrading commission. Give me liberty or give me death!"

From that hour I was no longer connected with the Government. But I had done the State some service and I sent in my bill:

Consultation with the Secretary of the Navy . . . . . . $ 50.00
Consultation with the Secretary of the Treasury . . .   50.00
Cabinet Consultation . . . . no charge
Salary as Clerk of the Senate Committee on
    Conchology, six days at $6 a day 36.00
                                Total $136.00

Not an item of this bill was paid, except the trifle of $36.00 for clerkship salary.

I was done with official life for the present. Let those clerks who were willing to be imposed on remain. Why, I know one who has to paste all sorts of little scraps into a scrapbook, sometimes as many as eight or ten scraps a day. He doesn't do it well, but he does it as well as he can. It is very fatiguing. It is exhausting to the intellect. Yet he only gets 1800 dollars a year. With a brain like his, that young man could amass thousands of dollars in some other pursuit, if he chose to do it. But no—his heart is with his country, and he will serve her as long as she has got a scrapbook left. And I know clerks that don't know how to write very well, but such knowledge as they possess they nobly lay at the feet of

their country, and toil on and suffer for 2500 dollars a year.
What they write has to be written over again by other clerks
sometimes; but when a man has done his best for his country,
should his country complain? Then there are clerks that have
no clerkship, and are waiting, and waiting, and waiting, for
a vacancy—waiting patiently for a chance to help their country out—and while they are waiting they only get barely
2000 dollars a year for it. It is sad. When a member of Congress has a friend, or a relative, who is gifted, but has no
employment wherein his great powers may be brought to
bear, he confers him upon his country, and gives him a clerkship in a department.⁶⁶ Why, when I think of those multitudes of clerks and Congressmen—whole families of them
—down there slaving away and keeping the country *together*,
why then I know in my heart there is something so good and
motherly about Washington, that grand old benevolent National Asylum for the Helpless.⁶⁷

I've just been reading an article in the newspaper which
has so impressed me that I've got to tell you about it. The
article speaks with enthusiasm about our railroad system and
its splendid record of achievement. It says that the trains
only destroyed—let me see—three thousand and seventy lives
last year by collisions, and twenty-seven thousand two hundred and sixty by running over heedless and unnecessary
people at crossings.

Now the companies seriously regretted the killing of these
people and went so far as to pay for some of them. I think
we can all be glad that the railway companies are disposed
to do the right and kindly thing, without compulsion. I know
of one instance which touched me greatly at the time. After
an accident the company sent home the remains of a dear

distant old relative of mine in a basket, with a note which read: "Please state what figure you hold him at—and return the basket." There couldn't be anything friendlier than that.[68]

I have recently been made a director of an accident insurance company, and when I read about things like that I'm convinced that there is no field for human effort nobler than the insurance business—especially accident insurance.

My home is in Hartford, which, as you know, is a city whose fame as an insurance center has spread to all parts of the world. As a matter of fact, we citizens of Hartford have got the reputation of being a triple band of brothers working sweetly hand-in-hand. First, the Colt Arms Company making the destruction of our race easy and convenient; second, our life insurance companies paying for the victims when they pass away; third, our fire insurance comrades taking care of their hereafter.

The fact is, ever since I've been a director in that accident insurance company I've felt that I'm a better man. Accidents have assumed a kindlier aspect. Distressing ones have lost half their horror. I look upon a cripple now with affectionate interest—as an advertisement. I don't seem to care for poetry anymore. I don't care for politics. Even agriculture doesn't excite me. But there is a charm about a railway collision that is unspeakable.[69]

And I have developed a new presence of mind in accidents. Not so long ago I was at a fire and happened to recognize one of our elderly clients leaning out of a fourth story window, calling for help. Everybody in the crowd looked up, but nobody did anything. Nobody had any presence of mind —nobody but me. I came to the rescue. I yelled for a rope. When it came I threw one end of it up to the old man. He caught it and I told him to tie it around his waist. He did so, and I pulled him down.[70]

No, there is nothing more beneficial than accident insurance. I've seen an entire family lifted out of poverty and into affluence by the simple boon of a broken leg. I've had people come to me on crutches, with tears in their eyes, to bless this beneficent institution. In all my experience of life, I've seen nothing so seraphic as the look which comes into a freshly mutilated man's face when he feels in his vest pocket with his remaining hand and finds his accident ticket all right.

I may as well say, too, by way of advertisement, that the noble charity to which I have become attached, as a director, is to be depended on. No man can take out a policy with us and not get crippled before the year is out. There was one poor fellow who had been disappointed so often by other companies that he'd grown disheartened—his appetite had left him, he'd ceased to smile, said life was just a weariness. Three weeks ago I got him to insure with us and now he's the brightest, happiest spirit in this land—has a good steady income and a stylish suit of new bandages every day, and travels around on a shutter.[71]

And we've had some of the most unusual cases come into that charity—the kind that never seem to happen the same way twice. One poor fellow got himself killed on the Fourth of July. Full of patriotism, he opened his mouth to hurrah and a rocket went down his throat. Before he could ask for a drink of water to quench the thing, it blew up and scattered him all over ... really, now, this is true—I know about it myself—twenty-four hours after that it was raining buttons, recognizable as his, on the Atlantic seaboard, fifteen hundred miles away. A person cannot have a disaster like that and be entirely cheerful the rest of his life.

I had an uncle, on an entirely different Fourth of July,

who was blown up that way, and—really—it trimmed him as it would a tree. Had hardly a limb left on him, anywhere. All we have now is an expurgated edition of that uncle.[72]

We have other testimonials, too; such as the case of the poor man who went to visit a dentist, a certain Dr. Tushmaker, to have his tooth out. Tushmaker pulled, the tooth didn't come—but the patient's right leg went up. The dentist said:

"What are you doing that for?"

"Because I can't help it!"

"You come back in a week and I'll take care of you."

During the week the doctor invented an instrument combining the properties of the lever, the screw, the wedge, the hammer, and the inclined plane. The patient came back. One turn of the crank, and out came the tooth. Its roots were hooked under the patient's right big toe and his whole skeleton was extracted with the tooth. They sent him home in a pillowcase.[73]

Now just let me read some statistics to you which ought to prove enlightening.

"One million of us die annually. Out of this million ten or twelve thousand are shot, stabbed, drowned, hanged, poisoned, or meet a similarly violent death in some other popular way. The Erie railroad kills from 23 to 46; the other 845 railroads kill an average of one-third of a man each; and the rest of that million, amounting in the aggregate to the appalling figure of 987,031 corpses, die naturally in their beds!"

You will excuse me from taking any more chances on those beds. The railroads are good enough for me.[74]

I once met a man on a train who told me the story of the most cheerless train ride I have ever heard described. He said that he was from Cleveland, Ohio, and that one stormy winter's night he had undertaken the sorrowful task of transporting the mortal remains of a boyhood friend back to a little town in Wisconsin to be buried. He said:

"I went down to the railroad station in a driving snowstorm and made arrangements for the long white-pine box to be put aboard the express car. Then I went inside to get some cigars. While I was gone a terrible mistake was made. The young fellow in charge of labelling cargo got my box confused with another long pine box containing guns to be shipped to a rifle company in Peoria. So that, unbeknownst to me, I was carrying a box of rifles; and my deceased friend was on his way to the rifle company in Peoria.

"The conductor sang out 'All aboard.' I jumped into the express car where my box was (or what I thought was my box) and got a comfortable seat on a bale of buckets. Just as we started off, a man skipped into the car and set a package of mature and capable Limburger cheese on one end of my coffin box—I mean my box of guns. That is to say, I know *now* it was Limburger cheese, but at the time I was wholly ignorant of what the package contained.

"We started off. The expressman made a brisk remark or two about the arctic weather, slammed his sliding doors shut, bolted them, and closed his window down tight, all the time contentedly humming 'Sweet By and By,' in a low tone and flatting a good deal.

"Presently I began to detect a most evil and searching odor stealing about on the frozen air. There was something infinitely saddening about my dear departed friend calling himself to my remembrance in this dumb, pathetic way, and it was hard to keep the tears back. Then, too, I was afraid the old expressman might notice it and that distressed me. But he just went humming tranquilly on and gave no sign. For this I was grateful, but uneasy, for every minute that went by the odor began to thicken up and get more and more gamey and hard to stand.

"Presently, the expressman got some wood together and made up a tremendous fire in his stove. I couldn't help feeling this was a mistake. Thompson—that was the expressman's name—went poking round the car, stuffing up cracks and saying that he didn't care how bad a night it was outside, he calculated to make *us* comfortable, anyway. I said nothing, but I believed he was not choosing the right way. Meantime he was humming to himself and the stove was getting hotter and hotter, and the place closer and closer. I felt myself growing pale and qualmish, and soon I noticed that 'Sweet By and By' was gradually fading out. Pretty soon it ceased altogether and there was an ominous stillness. Finally Thompson said:

" 'Friend of yours?'

"I said yes, with a sigh.

" 'He's pretty ripe, ain't he?'

"I said nothing. For a couple of minutes we were each busy with our own thoughts. Then Thompson said, in a low, awed voice:

" 'Sometimes it's uncertain whether they're really gone or not. *Seem* gone, you know—body warm, joints limber, and so even though you think they're gone, you don't really know. I've had cases in my car. It's perfectly awful; because *you* don't know what minute they'll rise up and look at you! But *he* ain't in no trance! No, sir, I'd go bail for him.'

"We sat for awhile, listening to the wind and the roar of the train.

" 'Well-a-well, we've all got to go, they ain't no getting around it. Man that is born of woman is of few days and far between, as Scriptur' says. All's got to go—just *everybody*, as you may say. . . . One day you're hearty and strong'—here he scrambled to his feet and broke a windowpane and stretched his nose out at it a moment or two. Then he sat down while I struggled up and thrust my nose out at the same place.

" 'What did he die of?' said Thompson.

"I said I didn't know.

" 'How long's he been dead?'

"It seemed a good idea to enlarge the facts to fit the probabilities, so I said, 'Two or three days.'

"Thompson gave me a look which plainly said, 'Two or three years, you mean.' Then he commenced to give his views about the unwisdom of putting off burials too long. He lounged off toward the box, stood by the cheese for a moment, then came back on a sharp trot and visited the broken pane.

" 'Twould a been a dum sight better all around if they'd started him along last summer.'

"Thompson sat down and buried his face in his red silk handkerchief, and began to slowly sway and rock his body like one who is doing his best to endure the almost unendurable. His face was turning gray. I knew mine hadn't any color left in it. By and by Thompson rested his forehead on his hand and sort of waved his handkerchief toward the box:

" 'I've carried many a one of 'em—some of 'em considerable overdue, too—but, lordy, he just lays over all of 'em, and does it easy. Cap, they were heliotrope to *him!*'

"It was plain something had to be done. I suggested cigars and Thompson thought it was a good idea. 'Likely it'll modify him some.'

"We puffed gingerly along for awhile, and tried hard to imagine that things were improved. But it wasn't any use. Before very long, and without any consultation both cigars were quietly dropped from our nerveless fingers at the same moment. Thompson said, with a sigh:

" 'No, Cap, it doesn't modify him worth a cent. Fact is, it makes him worse, becuz it appears to stir up his ambition. What do you reckon we better do now?'

"I wasn't able to suggest anything because I had to be swallowing and swallowing all the time, and I didn't like to trust myself to speak. Thompson fell to maundering about the miserable experiences of this night, and he began to refer to my poor friend by various titles—sometimes military ones, sometimes civil. I noticed that as fast as my poor friend's effectiveness grew, Thompson promoted him—gave him a bigger title. Finally he said:

" 'I've got an idea. Suppos'n we buckle down to it and give the Colonel a bit of a shove towards the other end of the car? —about ten foot say. He wouldn't have so much influence then, don't you reckon?'

"I said it was a good scheme. So we took in a good fresh breath at the broken pane, calculating to hold it till we got through. Then we bent over the deadly cheese and took a grip on the box. Thompson nodded 'ready' and we threw ourselves forward with all our might. But Thompson slipped and slumped down with his nose on the cheese, and his breath got loose. He gagged and gasped, and floundered up and made a break for the door, pawing the air and saying hoarsely:

" 'Don't hender me!—gimme the road! I'm a-dyin'; gimme the road!'

"Out on the cold platform I sat down and held his head awhile, and he revived. Presently he said:

" 'Do you reckon we started the General any?'

"I said no, we hadn't budged him.

" 'Well, then *that* idea's up the flume. We got to think of something else. He's suited where he is, I reckon, and if that's the way he feels about it, and has made up his mind he don't wish to be disturbed, you can bet he's going to have his own way in the business. Yes, better leave him right wher' he is, long as he wants it so. Because he holds all the trumps, don't you know, so it stands to reason any man that lays out to alter his plans for him is going to get left.'

"But we couldn't stay out there in that mad storm; we'd have frozen to death. So we went in and shut the door and began to suffer again, taking turns at the break in the window. When we stopped at a station Thompson went out, and just as we started off he pranced in cheerily and exclaimed:

" 'We're all right now. I reckon we've got the Commodore this time. I've got the stuff here that'll take the tuck out of him.'

"It was carbolic acid. He had a carboy of it. He sprinkled it all around everywhere; drenched everything with it: rifle-box, cheese, and all. Then we sat down feeling pretty hopeful. But it wasn't for long. The two perfumes began to mix and then—well, pretty soon we made a break for the door again. Thompson said in a kind of disheartened way:

" 'It ain't no use. We can't buck *him*. He just utilizes every-thing we put up to modify him with, and gives it his own flavor and plays it back on us, don't you know. I never did see one of 'em warm up to his work so and take such a dumnation interest in it.'

"In about an hour we stopped at another station, and just as we left Thompson came in with a bag.

" 'Cap, I'm goin' to chance him once more—just this once. And if we don't fetch him this time, the thing for us to do is to just throw up the sponge and withdraw from the canvas. That's the way *I* see it, anyway.'

"In the bag he had a lot of chicken feathers and dried ap-ples, and leaf tobacco and rags, and old shoes, and sulphur, and asafoetida and one thing or another. He piled them on a breadth of sheet iron in the middle of the floor and set fire to them.

"When they got well started I couldn't see, myself, how even the corpse could stand it. All that went before was just simply poetry to this smell—but, mind you, the original smell stood up out of it just as sublime as ever—in fact, these other smells just seemed to give it a better hold. And my, how rich it was! But I didn't make these reflections there—there wasn't time. We broke for the door and got wedged together in it trying to get out, and Thompson fell and got suffocated. I dragged him out by the collar, and I was mighty near gone myself.

"When he revived Thompson said, very dejectedly:

" 'We got to stay out here, Cap, frozen or not. We got to do it. There ain't no other way. The Governor wants to travel alone, and he's fixed it so he can outvote us. And, don't you know, we're poisoned? It's our last trip, you can make up your mind to it. Typhoid fever is what's going to come out of this. I feel it comin' right now.' " [75]

There is one disease which is sure to affect everybody at some time during his life, the disease that prompts a man to learn a foreign language. I escaped that infection for a long time; but I did not escape it entirely. I had learned a smattering of Chinese, one or two Indian dialects, and some other kindred classic languages, but nothing serious. The serious part came later when I went to Germany with an evil instinct that I could learn the German language. I know better now. I went to work at it, fought a good, honest fight with it, but the German language has been in the business longer than I have, and it came out ahead. [76]

The inventor of the language seems to have taken pleasure

in complicating it in every way he could think of. In the dis-
tribution of gender, for example: in German, a young lady has
no sex, while a turnip has. Think what overwrought reverence
that shows for the turnip and what callous disrespect for the
girl. Hear how it sounds. I translate from a conversation in
one of the best German Sunday-school books:

GRETCHEN: Wilhelm, where is the turnip?

WILHELM: She has gone to the kitchen.

GRETCHEN: Where is the beautiful English maiden?

WILHELM: It has gone to the opera.

To continue: a person's mouth, neck, bosom, elbows, fingers, nails, feet, and body are of the male sex, and his head
is male or neuter according to the word used to signify it, and
not according to the sex of the individual who wears it; for
in Germany all the women wear either male heads or sexless
ones; a person's nose, lips, shoulders, breast, hands, hips, and
toes are of the female sex; and his hair, ears, eyes, chin, knees,
heart, and conscience haven't any sex at all. The inventor of
the language probably got what he knew about a conscience
from hearsay.

Now, by this dissection, you will see that in Germany a
man may *think* he is a man, but when he comes to look into
the matter closely he is bound to have his doubts. He finds
that, in sober truth, he is a mixture; and if he tries to comfort
himself with the thought that at least one-third of him is
masculine, he will quickly remember that in this respect he
is no better off than any woman or cow in the land.

It is true that by some oversight of the inventor of this
language, a woman is female; but a wife is not—which is unfortunate. A wife has no sex; she is neuter.

Another troublesome aspect of the German language is the
parenthesis distemper. There are several variations of this
disease, but I can show you what I mean by using one of

them. I refer to the kind of parenthesis which results from splitting the verb in two, and putting half of it at the beginning of an exciting paragraph and the other half at the end of it. A favorite one is *reiste ab*—which means departed. Here is an example, reduced to English:

"The trunks now being ready, he DE—after kissing his mother and sisters, and once more pressing to his bosom his adored Gretchen, who, dressed in a simple white muslin, with a single tube rose in the ample folds of her rich brown hair, had tottered feebly down the stairs, still pale from the terror and excitement of the past evening, but longing to lay her poor aching head yet once again upon the breast of him whom she loved more dearly than life itself—PARTED."

Let the candidate for the asylum try to grapple with that and see how soon he'll be elected! If it doesn't soften his brain, it'll petrify it.

There are some exceedingly useful words in this language, Schlag, for example, and Zug. There are three-quarters of a column of Schlags in the dictionary, and a column and a half of Zugs. The word Schlag means Blow—Hit, Slap, Time, Coin, Stamp, Apoplexy, Forest Clearing. This is its simple and exact meaning—that is to say, its restricted, its fettered meaning. But there are ways by which you can set it free so that it can soar away, and never be at rest. You can hang any word you please to its tail, and make it mean anything you want to. You can begin with Schlag-ader, which means artery, and you can hang on the whole dictionary, word by word, clear through the alphabet to Schlagwasser, which means bilge-water.

Just the same with Zug. Strictly speaking, Zug means Pull, March, Direction, Touch, Line, Flourish, Trait of Character, Organ-stop, Whiff, Chess-move. And so on. The thing which it does *not* mean is yet to be discovered.

One cannot overestimate the usefulness of Schlag and Zug. Armed with just these two, and the word Also, think what you can accomplish? The German word Also is the equivalent of the English phrase, "you know."

Now the foreigner, equipped with these three words, is master of the situation. Let him talk right along fearlessly; let him pour his indifferent German forth, and when he lacks for a word let him heave a Schlag into the vacuum. The chances are it'll fit like a plug. But if it doesn't, let him promptly heave a Zug after it; the two of them together can hardly fail to bung the hole. But, if by a miracle, they *should* fail, let him simply say "Also!" and this will give him time to think. In Germany, when you load your conversational gun, it is always best to throw in a few Schlags and Zugs; because it doesn't make any difference how much the rest of the charge may scatter, you are bound to bag something with them. Then you blandly say "Also" and load up again.

I have heard of an American student who was asked how he was getting along with his German, and who answered promptly, "I am not getting along at all. I have worked at it hard for three level months, and all I've got to show for it is one solitary German phrase—Zwei glas—two glasses of beer." But I would rather decline those two drinks than one German verb." [78]

Now, having pointed out several of the vices of this language, it is only fair that I point out a virtue. There are some German words which are powerfully effective. Those which deal with love, in any and all forms, from honest good-will clear up to courtship; those which deal with out-door nature, in its softest and loveliest aspects—with meadows and forests, the fragrance and sunshine of summer, and the moonlight of peaceful winter nights; and lastly and chiefly, in those words which express pathos is the language surpassingly rich and effective. There are German songs which can make a stranger to the language cry.[79]

But let us hope that when the gentleman who invented the German language tries again he will come up with one good square responsible sex, instead of a language in which the Fish is a He, the Scales are She, and the Fishwife It.[80]

My studies have convinced me that a truly gifted person may learn the German language in thirty years. Others will take longer. If the German language is to remain as it is, without being trimmed down and repaired, then it ought to be gently and reverently laid aside among the other dead languages, for only the dead have time to learn it.[81]

It has seemed to me that what we lack in our system of education is some definite yardstick by which a student can measure his progress from day to day. Take for instance, the system involved in learning to ride a bicycle. Now in this case the steps of one's progress are distinctly marked. At the end of each lesson the student *knows* he has acquired something; and he also knows what that something is; and likewise that it had better stay with him. It is not like studying German, where you mull along in a groping, uncertain way for thirty years, and at last, just as you think you've got it, they spring the subjunctive on you. And there you are. No, I see now plainly enough that the great pity of the German language is that you can't fall off it and hurt yourself. There is nothing like that feature to make you attend strictly to business.[82]

Last spring I gave into age for the first time by mounting spectacles. And on that very same day I renewed my youth by mounting a bicycle for the first time. The spectacles stayed on.[83]

An Expert Rider in our neighborhood said he would teach

me. So I went down and bought a barrel of liniment and a bicycle. The Expert came home with me, to instruct me. We chose the back yard, for the sake of privacy, and went to work.

Mine wasn't a full-grown bicycle, just a colt. It had a front wheel that came up about this high; the little tiny back wheel was way down in the stern; the saddle hung out here somewhere, with the tiller just in front of it. The Expert got up on its back and rode around a little, to show me how easy it was to do. He said the dismounting was perhaps the hardest thing to learn, so we'd leave that until last. But he was wrong. All he needed to do was to get me on the machine and stand out of the way. I could get off myself. Inexperienced as I was, I dismounted in the best time on record. He was on that side at the time, shoving up the machine. We all came down with a crash, the Expert on the bottom, me next, and the machine on top.

We examined the machine, but it wasn't injured. This time the Expert shoved up on the other side, but I dismounted on that side, so the result was the same as before.

The machine wasn't hurt. This time the Expert took up a sheltered position behind, but somehow or other we landed on him again. He was full of surprise and admiration. Said it was abnormal. The machine was all right, not a scratch on her. We applied a little oil and the Expert limped out to position again. This time he took up the position of short-stop and got another man to shove up behind. We got up a good deal of speed and then traversed a brick. I went over the top of the tiller and landed on the instructor's back, and saw the machine fluttering in the air between me and the sun. It was a good thing it came down on us, for that broke the fall and it wasn't injured.

When the Expert got out of the hospital a week or so later,

he brought four assistants with him, and we went to work again. I began to make progress. I got to the point where I could balance the machine fairly well, and steer it. The next task was learning to mount it. You do it this way: you hop along behind it on your right foot, resting the other on the mounting peg and grasping the tiller with your hands. You rise on the peg, stiffen your left leg, hang your other one around in the air, lean your stomach against the rear of the saddle, and then fall off. Maybe on one side, maybe the other. But you fall off.

You get up and do it again. You steer along, straight ahead, rise forward, bring your right leg and then your body into the saddle, catch your breath, fetch a violent hitch this way and that, and down you go again. Six more falls make you perfect.

Next you come to the voluntary dismount. That other kind, the involuntary one, that was easy. In the voluntary dismount you get off as you would from a horse. Now that seems easy too, but it isn't. The fact is you don't get down as you would from a horse, at all. You get down as you would from a house afire. You make a spectacle of yourself every time.

At the end of eight days I was graduated, in the rough. That meant I could paddle my own bicycle without outside help. Before taking final leave of me, the Expert inquired concerning my physical strength, and I was able to inform him I hadn't any. I showed him my biceps. He ran his hand over one of them and said that in the dark it might be mistaken for an oyster in a rag.

Then he left me and I started out alone to seek adventures. You don't really have to seek them—that's just a phrase. They come to you. I chose a quiet back street which was about thirty yards wide between the curbstones. I knew it wasn't wide enough, but I figured if I kept strict watch I could crowd through.

Of course, I had trouble mounting the machine, with no encouragement. I was about to give up when I noticed a boy watching me. He was full of interest and comment. The first time I went down he said if he was me he'd dress up in pillows. The second time he advised me to go learn to ride a tricycle first. I began to get angry at him. The third time I collapsed he laughed. But the next time I succeeded, and got under way, occupying pretty much all of the street. The boy followed me, from a safe distance, commenting. A little girl passed by, balancing a washboard on her head, and giggled. The boy said, "Let him alone, he's going to a funeral." I struck a hill and began to pant and perspire and the boy said, "Take it easy—there ain't no hurry. They can't hold the funeral without you."

Pretty soon I saw a wagon coming towards me, loaded with cabbages. It was coming straight down the center of the road, with only fourteen or fifteen yards of space on either side. I was petrified. I couldn't shout at the driver—a beginner can't shout. If he opens his mouth, he's gone.

In this grisly emergency the boy came to the rescue, and for once I was grateful to him. He kept a sharp lookout on the gyrations of my bicycle, and shouted to the driver:

"To the left! Turn to the left or this jackass'll run over you!" The driver started to do it. "No, to the right, to the right! Hold on—to the left now!—To the right!—to the *left!*—right! Left! Ri—Stay where you are, or you're a goner!"

I caught the off horse in the starboard and went down in a pile.

Within the next five days I made so much progress the boy couldn't keep up with me. He finally had to go back and sit down on his front porch, and watch me fall at long range.

There was one place I always had trouble. It was where there was a row of stones across one end of the street. Even after I got to the point where I could steer pretty good, I was so afraid of those stones I always hit them. They gave me the worst falls I ever got. Except those I got from dogs. I've heard it said that no expert is quick enough to run over a dog, that the dog will always be able to skip out of his way in time. That may be true, but I think the reason *he* can't run over the dog is because he is trying to. I didn't try to run over any dog. But I ran over every dog that came along. I think that's the real difference. If you *try* to run over the dog, he knows how to calculate. But if you try to *miss* him, he doesn't know how to calculate and he's liable to jump the wrong way every time. It was always so in my experience. Even when I couldn't hit a wagon I could hit a dog that came to see me practice. They liked to see me practice, and they all came. There was very little going on in our neighborhood to entertain a dog.

I can steer as well as I want to, now, and I'll catch that boy out one of these days and run over *him* if he doesn't reform.

I suppose I could have learned to ride that bicycle without a teacher, but it would have been more perilous. The self-taught man seldom knows anything accurately, and he does not know a tenth as much as he could have known if he had worked under teachers. There are those of us who imagine that the unlucky accidents of life—life's experiences, as we call them—are in some way useful to us. I wish I could find out how. I never knew one of them to happen twice; they always change off and swap around and catch you on your inexperienced side. If personal experience can be worth anything in an education, it wouldn't seem likely that you could trip Methuselah, and yet if that old person could come back here now it's more than likely that one of the first things he'd do would be to take hold of one of these electric wires and tie himself all up in knots. Now the surer thing—the wiser thing—would be for him to ask somebody whether it was a good thing to take hold of. But that would not suit him. He would be one of the self-taught kind that go by experience; he'd want to examine for himself; and it would be useful to him; it would leave his education in quite a complete and rounded-out condition, till he got to bouncing a dynamite can around to find out what was in that. Get a teacher. It saves much time and liniment. Sometimes.[84]

Act Two

I'm often asked why I wear this white suit. Well, I've traveled around a good deal and I've mixed with royalty, and savages, and common ordinary people, and there is one thing that always struck me wherever I went: clothes make the man. Naked people have little or no influence in society.[1]

It seems to me that in the matter of intellect the ant must be a strangely overrated bird. During many summers, now, I have watched him, when I ought to have been doing something better, and I have not yet come across a living ant that seemed to have any more sense than a dead one. I refer to the ordinary ant, of course; I have had no experience of those wonderful Swiss and African ones which vote, keep drilled armies, hold slaves, and dispute about religion. Those particular ants may be all that the naturalist paints them, but I am persuaded that the average ant is a sham!

I admit his industry, of course. He is the hardest working creature in the world—when anybody is looking. His leather-headedness is the point I make against him. He goes out foraging, he makes a capture, and then what does he do? Go home? No, he goes anywhere but home. He doesn't know where home is. His home may be only three feet away—no matter, he can't find it. He makes his capture, as I have said; it is generally something which can be of no sort of use to himself or anybody else; it is usually seven times bigger than it ought to be; he hunts out the awkwardest place to take hold of it; he lifts it bodily up in the air by main force, and starts; not toward home, but in the opposite direction; not calmly and wisely, but with a frantic haste which is wasteful of his strength; he fetches up against a pebble, and instead of going around it, he climbs over it—backwards—dragging his booty after him, tumbles down on the other side, jumps up in a passion, kicks the dust off his clothes, moistens his hands, grabs his property viciously, yanks it this way, then that, shoves it ahead of him a moment, gets madder and madder, then presently hoists it into the air and goes tearing away in an entirely new direction; comes to a weed; it never occurs to him to go around it; no, he must climb it; and he does climb it; dragging his worthless property to the top—which is as bright a thing to do as it would be for me to carry a sack of flour from Heidelberg to Paris by way of Strasburg steeple; when he gets up there he finds that that is not the place; takes a cursory glance at the scenery and either climbs down again or tumbles down, and starts off once more—as usual, in a new direction. At the end of half an hour, he fetches up within six inches of the place he started from and lays his burden down; meantime he has been over all the ground for two yards around, and climbed all the weeds and pebbles he came across.

Now he wipes the sweat from his brow, strokes his limbs, and then marches aimlessly off, in as violent a hurry as ever. He traverses a good deal of zig-zag country, and by and by stumbles on his same booty again. He does not remember to have ever seen it before; he looks around to see which is not the way home, grabs his bundle and starts; he goes through the same adventures he had before; finally stops to rest, and a friend comes along. Evidently the friend remarks that a last year's grasshopper leg is a very noble acquisition, and inquires where he got it. Evidently the proprietor does not remember exactly where he did get it, but thinks he got it "around here somewhere." Evidently the friend contracts to help him freight it home. Then they take hold of opposite ends of that grasshopper leg and begin to tug with all their might in opposite directions.

Presently they take a rest and confer together. They decide that something is wrong, they can't make out what. Then they go at it again, just as before. Same result. Mutual recriminations follow. Evidently each accuses the other of being an obstructionist. They warm up, and the dispute ends in a fight. They lock themselves together and chew each other's jaws for a while; then they roll and tumble on the ground till one loses a horn or a leg and has to haul off for repairs. They make up and go to work again in the same old insane way, but the crippled ant is at a disadvantage; tug as he may, the other one drags off the booty and him at the end of it. Instead of giving up, he hangs on, and gets his shins bruised against every obstruction that comes in the way. By and by, when that grasshopper leg has been dragged all over the same old ground once more, it is finally dumped at about the spot where it originally lay, the two perspiring ants inspect it thoughtfully and decide that dried grasshopper legs are a poor sort of property after all, and then each starts off in a different direction to see if he can't find an old nail or something else that is heavy enough to afford entertainment and at the same time valueless enough to make an ant want to own it.

I measured the ground which these two asses traversed,

and arrived at the conclusion that what they had accomplished inside of twenty minutes would constitute some such job as this—relatively speaking, for a man to strap two eight-hundred-pound horses together, carry them eighteen hundred feet, mainly over (not around) boulders averaging six feet high, and in the course of the journey climb up and jump from the top of one precipice like Niagara, and three steeples, each a hundred and twenty feet high; and then put the horses down, in an exposed place, without anybody to watch them, and go off to indulge in some other idiotic miracle for vanity's sake.

Science has recently discovered that the ant does not lay up anything for winter use. This will knock him out of literature, to some extent. He does not work, except when people are looking, and only then when the observer has a green, naturalistic look and seems to be taking notes. This will injure him for the Sunday schools. He cannot stroll around a stump and find his way home again. This amounts to idiocy, and once the damaging fact is established, thoughtful people will cease to look up to him, the sentimental will cease to fondle him. His vaunted industry is but a vanity and of no effect, since he never gets home with anything he starts with. This disposes of the last remnant of his reputation and wholly destroys his main usefulness as a moral agent, since it will make the sluggard hesitate to go to him any more. It is strange, beyond comprehension, that so manifest a humbug as the ant has been able to fool so many nations and keep it up so many ages without being found out.

The ant is strong, but I saw another strong thing, where we had not suspected the presence of much muscular power before. A toadstool—that vegetable which springs to full growth in a single night—had torn loose and lifted a matted mass of pine needles and dirt of twice its own bulk into the air, and supported it there, like a column supporting a shed. Ten thousand toadstools, with the right purchase, could lift a man, I suppose. But what good would it do? [2]

Animals talk to each other, of course. There can be no question about that; but I suppose there are very few people who can understand them. I never knew but one man who could. I knew he could because he told me so himself. He was a middle-aged, simple-hearted miner who had lived in a lonely corner of California, among the woods and mountains, a good many years, and had studied the ways of his only neighbors, the beasts and the birds, until he believed he could accurately translate any remark which they made. This was Jim Baker. According to Jim Baker, some animals have only a limited education, and use only very simple words, and scarcely ever a comparison or a flowery figure; whereas, certain other animals have a large vocabulary, a fine command of language and a ready and fluent delivery; consequently these latter talk a great deal; they like it; they are conscious of their talent, and they enjoy "showing off." Baker said that after long and careful observation he had come to the conclusion that the bluejays were the best talkers to be found among birds and beasts. Said he:

"There's more *to* a bluejay than any other creature. He has got more moods, and more different kinds of feeling than other creatures; and, mind you, whatever a bluejay feels, he can put into language. And no mere commonplace language, either, but rattling, out-and-out book-talk—and bristling with metaphor, too—just bristling! And as for command of language—why, *you* never see a bluejay get stuck for a word. No man ever did. They just boil out of him! And another thing I've noticed a good deal: there's no bird, or cow, or anything that uses as good grammar as a bluejay. You may say a cat uses good grammar. Well, a cat does—but you let a cat get excited once; you let a cat get to pulling fur with another cat on a shed, nights, and you'll hear grammar that will give you the lockjaw. Ignorant people think it's the *noise* which fighting cats make that is so aggravating, but it ain't so; it's the sickening grammar they use. Now I've never heard a jay use bad grammar but very seldom; and when they do, they are as ashamed as a human; they shut right down and leave.

"You may call a jay a bird. Well, so he is, in a measure— because he's got feathers on him, and don't belong to no church, perhaps; but otherwise he is just as much a human as you be. And I'll tell you for why. A jay's gifts, and instincts, and feelings, and interests, cover the whole ground. A jay hasn't got any more principle than a Congressman. A jay will lie, a jay will steal, a jay will deceive, a jay will betray; and four times out of five, a jay will go back on his solemnest promise. The sacredness of an obligation is a thing which you can't cram into no bluejay's head. Now, on top of all this, there's another thing; a jay can outswear any gentleman in the mines. You think a cat can swear. Well, a cat can; but you give a bluejay a subject that calls for his reserve powers, and where is your cat? Don't talk to *me*—I know too much about this thing. And there's yet another thing; in the one little particular of scolding—just good, clean, out-and-out-scolding—a bluejay can lay over anything, human or divine. Yes, sir, a jay is everything that a man is. A jay can cry, a jay can laugh, a jay can feel shame, a jay can reason and plan and discuss, a jay likes gossip and scandal, a jay has got a sense of humor, a jay knows when he is an ass just as well as you do—maybe better. If a jay ain't human, he better take in his sign, that's all. Now I'm going to tell you a perfectly true fact about some bluejays.

"When I first begun to understand jay language correctly, there was a little incident happened here. Seven years ago, the last man in this region but me moved away. There stands his house—been empty ever since; a log house, with a plank roof—just one big room, and no more; no ceiling—nothing between the rafters and the floor. Well, one Sunday morning I was sitting out here in front of my cabin, with my cat, taking the sun, and looking at the blue hills, and listening to the leaves rustling so lonely in the trees, and thinking of the home away yonder in the states, that I hadn't heard from in thirteen years, when a bluejay lit on that house, with an acorn in his mouth, and says, 'Hello, I reckon I've struck something.' When he spoke, the acorn dropped out of his mouth and rolled down the roof, of course, but he didn't care; his mind was all on the thing he had struck. It was a knot-hole in the roof. He cocked his head to one side, shut one eye, and put the other one to the hole, like a 'possum looking down a jug; then he glanced up with his bright eyes, gave a wink or two with his wings—which signifies gratification, you understand—and says, 'It looks like a hole, it's located like a hole—blamed if I don't believe it *is* a hole!'

"Then he cocked his head down and took another look; he glances up perfectly joyful, this time; winks his wings and his tail both, and says, 'Oh, no, this ain't no fat thing, I reckon! If I ain't in luck!—why it's a perfectly elegant hole!' So he flew down and got that acorn, and fetched it up and dropped it in, and was just tilting his head back, with the heavenliest smile on his face, when all of a sudden he was paralyzed into a listening attitude and that smile faded gradually out of his countenance like breath off'n a razor, and the queerest look of surprise took its place. Then he says, 'Why, I didn't hear it fall!' He cocked his eye at the hole again, and took a long look; raised up and shook his head; stepped around to the other side of the hole and took another look from that side; shook his head again. He studied a while, then he just went into the *de*tails—walked round and round the hole and spied into it from every point of the compass. No use. Now he took a thinking attitude on the comb of the roof and scratched the back of his head with his right foot a minute, and finally says, 'Well, it's too many for *me,* that's certain; must be a mighty long hole; however, I ain't got no time to fool around here, I got to 'tend to business; I reckon it's all right—chance it anyway.'

"So he flew off and fetched another acorn and dropped it in, and tried to flirt his eye to the hole quick enough to see what become of it, but he was too late. He held his eye there as much as a minute; then he raised up and sighed, and says, 'Confound it, I don't seem to understand this thing, no way; however, I'll tackle her again.' He fetched another acorn, and done his level best to see what become of it, but he couldn't. He says, 'Well, *I* never struck no such a hole as this before; I'm of the opinion it's a totally new kind of a hole.' Then he begun to get mad. He held in for a spell, walking up and down the comb of the roof and shaking his head and muttering to himself; but his feelings got the upper hand of him, presently, and he broke loose and cussed himself black in the face. I never see a bird take on so about a little thing. When he got through he walks to the hole and looks in again for half a minute; then he says, 'Well, you're a long hole, and a deep hole, and a mighty singular hole altogether—but I've started in to fill you, and I'm damned if I *don't* fill you, if it takes a hundred years!'

"And with that, away he went. You never see a bird work so since you were born. The way he hove acorns into that hole for about two hours and a half was one of the most exciting and astonishing spectacles I ever struck. He never stopped to take a look any more—he just hove 'em in and went for more. Well, at last he could hardly flop his wings, he was so tuckered out. He comes a-drooping down, once more, sweating like an ice-pitcher, drops his acorn in and says, 'Now I guess I've got the bulge on you by this time!' So he bent down for a look. If you'll believe me, when his head come up again he was just pale with rage. He says, 'I've shoveled acorns enough in there to keep the family thirty years, and if I can see a sign of one of 'em I wish I may land in a museum with a belly full of sawdust in two minutes!'

"He just had strength enough to crawl up on the comb and lean his back again the chimbly, and then he collected his impressions and begun to free his mind. I see in a second that what I had mistook for profanity in the mines was only just the rudiments, as you might say.

"Another jay was going by, and heard him doing his devotions, and stops to inquire what was up. The sufferer told him the whole circumstance, and says, 'Now yonder's the hole, and if you don't believe me, go and look for yourself.' So this fellow went and looked, and comes back and says, 'How many did you say you put in there?' 'Not any less than two tons,' says the sufferer. The other jay went and looked again. He couldn't seem to make it out, so he raised a yell, and three more jays come. They all examined the hole, they all made the sufferer tell it over again, then they all discussed it, and got off as many leather-headed opinions about it as an average crowd of humans could have done.

"They called in more jays; then more and more, till pretty soon this whole region 'peared to have a blue flush about it. There must have been five thousand of them; and such another jawing and disputing and ripping and cussing, you never heard. Every jay in the whole lot put his eye to the hole and delivered a more chuckle-headed opinion about the mystery than the jay that went there before him. They examined the house all over, too. The door was standing half open, and at last one old jay happened to go and light on it and look in. Of course, that knocked the mystery galley-west in a second. There lay the acorns, scattered all over the floor. He flopped his wings and raised a whoop. 'Come here!' he says, 'Come here, everybody; hang'd if this fool hasn't been trying to fill up a house with acorns!' They all came a-swooping down like a blue cloud, and as each fellow lit on the door and took a glance, the whole absurdity of the contract that first jay had tackled hit him home and he fell over backwards suffocating with laughter, and the next jay took his place and done the same.

"Well, sir, they roosted around here on the housetop and the trees for an hour, and guffawed over that thing like human beings. It ain't any use to tell me a bluejay hasn't got a sense of humor, because I know better. And memory, too. They brought jays here from all over the United States to look down that hole, every summer for three years. Other birds, too. And they could all see the point, except an owl that come from Nova Scotia to visit the Yo Semite, and he took this thing in on his way back. He said he couldn't see anything funny in it. But then he was a good deal disappointed about Yo Semite, too." [3]

Although I had been raised in the most exclusive circles of Missouri, I had never attended the Wagnerian opera. So, in Germany, I went to Bayreuth and took in *Parsifal*. I shall never forget it. The first act occupied two hours and I enjoyed it, in spite of the singing. Though singing does seem the

wrong name to apply to it. In *Parsifal* there is a character by
the name of Guernemanz, a hermit, who stands on the stage
in one spot practicing by the hour, while first one character
and then another endures what he can of it, and then retires
to die.[4]

I found that there is nothing the Germans like so much
as opera. They like it wholeheartedly, as a result of habit
and education. Our nation will like the opera, too, by and by,
no doubt. One in fifty of those who attend our operas likes
it already, perhaps, but I think a good many of the other
forty-nine go there with the idea of learning to like it. This
was my case.

Some of those Wagnerian operas bang along for six whole
hours at a stretch. I remember the one called *Lohengrin*.
The banging and crashing was something beyond belief.
There wasn't much action; that is to say, there wasn't much
really done. It was only talked about, and always violently.
It was what you might call a narrative play. There wasn't
much of that customary thing where the tenor and soprano
stand down by the footlights, warbling, with blended voices,
holding their arms out towards each other and drawing them
back, and spreading both hands over first one breast and
then the other with a shake and a pressure; in this piece it
was every rioter for himself and no blending. Each one sang
out his grievance in turn, accompanied by the whole orches-
tra of sixty instruments, and just when one was hoping they
might come to some understanding and modify the noise,
a great chorus composed entirely of maniacs would suddenly
break forth, and during the next two minutes, and sometimes
three, I lived over again all I'd suffered the time the orphan
asylum burnt down.

We had just one brief little season of heaven during all
this long and diligent reproduction of the other place. That

was in the third act, when a gorgeous procession of people marched around and sang the Wedding Chorus. To my untutored ears, that was music—divine music. While my seared soul was steeped in the healing balm of this passage it seemed to me that I could almost suffer again the torments that had gone before. But there is where the deep ingenuity of the opera is revealed. They deal so much in sorrow and suffering that these calm passages sound sweeter by contrast. I suppose a pleasant air in an opera sounds prettier there than it would elsewhere; just as an honest man shines more in politics than he would anywhere else.[5]

I went to that opera with an old dowager lady. She asked me to sit in her box and I did. She talked through the whole thing, humming the tunes and singing the verses. When it was over she asked me if I'd care to hear *Aida* with her the following week and I said, "I'd be delighted. I've never heard you in that." [6]

One thing I noticed about the German opera is that they hardly ever encore a song, even though the audience might be dying to hear it again. This was a blessing I had not expected and I was grateful. Apparently, demanding an encore is not considered good breeding, so only Kings can demand encores. With them, it's all right. It pleases everyone to see the King pleased. Still, there are circumstances where even a royal encore— But let me give you an example.

The King of Bavaria is a poet, with all the eccentricities that go along with that occupation—with the advantage of being able to gratify them. He is fond of the opera, but not fond of sitting in the presence of an audience. So, occasionally, while the players are in the midst of removing their paint and finery, a command from the King comes and they put it back on again and they have to perform the whole opera over again for that one solitary figure.

Once, this poet-King took an odd freak into his head. High above the stage of the theatre there is a maze of water pipes, so pierced that in case of fire streams of water can be let loose on it; if necessary it can be increased to a regular flood.

The poet-King was the sole audience. The opera proceeded, it was one with a storm in it, the mimic thunder began to mutter, the mimic wind began to wail, the mimic rain pattered. The King's interest rose higher. He became enthusiastic. He cried out:

"Good—very good! But I will have real rain. Turn on the water."

The manager pleaded with him but the King insisted.

"I will have real rain. Turn on the water!"

So the real rain was turned on and began to descend while the actors and actresses tripped about singing bravely and pretending not to notice. The King was delighted.

"Bravo, bravo," he cried. "More thunder. More lightning. Turn on more rain."

The thunder boomed, the lightning glared, and the deluge poured down. The mimic royalty on the stage, with their soaked satins clinging to their bodies, slopped around, ankle deep in water, warbling as best they could, while the fiddlers under the eaves of the stage sawed away for dear life, with the cold overflow spouting down on the backs of their necks, and the dry, happy King sat in his box and wore his gloves to ribbons applauding.

"More yet!" he cried. "Let loose all the thunder, turn on all the water! I'll hang the man who raises an umbrella!"

It was the most tremendous storm ever produced in any theatre. Finally it was over. The King was in ecstasy.

"Magnificent, magnificent!" he cried. "Encore! Do it again!"

On the third encore the chief tenor went under, and this ended the performance.[7]

There is one thing you want to sample if you go to Bayreuth, and that is the food. Photographs fade, busts of Wagner get broken, but once you absorb a Bayreuth-restaurant meal it is your possession and property until the time comes to embalm the rest of you.[8]

Much as the modern French duel is ridiculed by certain smart people, it is really one of the most dangerous institutions of our day. Since it is always fought in the open air, the combatants are nearly sure to catch cold.

As soon as I heard about the latest fiery outbreak between my friend, M. Gambetta, and M. Fourtou in the French Assembly, I knew that trouble was sure to follow. Gambetta was a huge man with a desperate and implacable nature, and I knew the thirst for revenge would penetrate to the remotest frontiers of his person.

I didn't wait for him to call on me, but went to him at once. I found him steeped in a profound French calm. He was moving swiftly back and forth among the debris of his furniture, halting every little while to deposit another handful of his hair on the pile he'd been building of it on the table.

He threw his arms around my neck, bent me over his stomach to his breast, kissed me on both cheeks and hugged me four or five times, and then placed me in his own armchair. As soon as I had got well again, I said I supposed he would want me to act as his second. He said, "Of course!" I said, "First we'll draw up the will." He said he'd never heard of a man in his right mind doing anything of the kind, but I insisted on it and stuck to my point. Then we went on to a choice of his last words. He thought awhile and wanted to know how this struck me, as a dying exclamation:

"I die for my God, for my country, for freedom of speech, for progress, and the universal brotherhood of man!"

I told him I thought this was a good speech for a consumptive, but it would require too lingering a death for the field of honor. So he finally cut it down to this, which he copied in his memorandum book, intending to get it by heart:

"I die that France may live."

I told him this seemed to lack relevancy, but he said that didn't matter in last words; what you wanted was thrill.

Next came the choice of weapons. He said he wasn't feeling too well and would leave that to me. So I wrote the following note and took it to M. Fourtou's second:

"Sir: M. Gambetta accepts M. Fourtou's challenge and authorizes me to propose Plessis-Piquet as the place of meeting; tomorrow morning at daybreak as the time; and axes as the weapons. I am, sir, with great respect, Mark Twain."

M. Fourtou's friend read it and shuddered. Then he said:

"Have you considered, sir, what would be the inevitable result of such a meeting as this?"

"Well, for instance, what would it be?"

"Bloodshed!"

"Well, that's about the size of it," I told him. "What was your side proposing to shed?"

I had him there. He saw he'd made a blunder, so he tried to explain it away. He said he and his principal would enjoy axes, in fact prefer them, but they were barred by the French code. I suggested Gatling guns at fifteen paces, but the code was in the way again. So I proposed rifles; then double-barrelled shotguns, then brickbats at three-quarters of a mile. They were all rejected. I said:

"Perhaps *you* would be good enough to suggest a weapon."

He brightened up and started hunting in his pockets—pocket after pocket—muttering all the while, "Now what could I have done with them?"

At last he fished out of his vest pocket a couple of little things which I carried to the light and found to be pistols. They were single-barrelled and silver-mounted, and very dainty and pretty. I wasn't able to speak for emotion. I hung one on my watch chain and gave back the other to him. Then he unrolled a postage stamp containing several cartridges and gave me one of them. I begged him to go on and suggest a distance and he said sixty-five yards. By this time my mind was growing weak and confused under the strain and I lost patience with him.

"Sixty-five yards with these instruments? Squirt guns would be deadlier at fifty!" But I was only able to get him to reduce the distance to thirty-five yards.

There was nothing for me to do but go home to my old lionheart and tell him the humiliating story. When I entered, M. Gambetta was laying the last lock of his hair on the altar. He sprang towards me as soon as he saw me:

"You have made the fatal arrangements—I see it in your eye!"

"I have."

His face paled a trifle and he leaned on the table for support.

"The weapon. Quick, what is it?"

"This!" And I showed him the silver-mounted thing. He glanced at it and swooned ponderously to the floor. When he came to, he said mournfully:

"The unnatural calm to which I have subjected myself has told upon my nerves. But away with weakness! I will confront my fate like a man and a Frenchman." He struggled up to his feet and assumed an attitude which for sublimity has seldom been surpassed by statues. "Behold, I am calm, I am ready. Reveal to me the distance?"

"Thirty-five yards."

I could not lift him up, of course. But I rolled him over and poured water down his back and he presently came to.

"Thirty-five yards, without a rest? Was nothing said about that man's family standing up with him, to offset my bulk? But no matter. I would not stoop to make such a suggestion. If he is not noble enough to suggest it himself, he is welcome to this advantage. Mark you one thing! In my fall the world shall see how the chivalry of France meets death."

He now sank into a sort of stupor of reflection, which lasted some minutes; after which he broke silence with:

"The hour—what is the hour fixed for the collision?"

"Dawn, tomorrow."

He seemed greatly surprised.

"Insanity! I never heard of such a thing. Nobody is abroad at such an hour."

"That is the reason I named it. Do you mean to say you want an audience?"

"It is no time to bandy words. I am astonished that M. Fourtou should have agreed to so strange an innovation. Go at once and require a later hour."

I ran downstairs, threw open the front door, and almost plunged into the arms of M. Fourtou's second. He said:

"I have the honor to say that my principal strenuously objects to the hour chosen, and begs you will consent to change it to half past nine."

"Any courtesy, sir, which it is in our power to extend is at the service of your excellent principal. We agree to the proposed change of time."

"I beg you to accept the thanks of my client."

Then he turned to a person behind him, and said:

"You hear, M. Noir, the hour is altered to half past nine."

Whereupon M. Noir bowed, expressed his thanks, and went away.

My accomplice continued:

"Have you engaged a hearse?"

"Bless my stupidity, I never thought of it! I will attend to it right away. I must seem very ignorant to you; but you must try to overlook that, because I have never had any experience with such a swell duel as this before. I have had a good deal to do with duels on the Pacific Coast, but I see now that they were crude affairs. A hearse—sho! we used to leave the elected lying around loose, and let anybody cord them up and cart them off that wanted to."

I returned to my client, who said, "Very well; at what hour is the engagement to begin?"

"Half past nine."

"Very good indeed. Have you sent the fact to the newspapers?"

"*Sir!* If after our long and intimate friendship you can for a moment deem me capable of so base a treachery—"

"Tut, tut! What words are these, my dear friend? Have I wounded you? Ah, forgive me; I am overloading you with labor. Therefore go on with the other details, and drop this one from your list. The bloody-minded Fourtou will be sure to attend to it. Or I myself—yes, to make certain, I will drop a note to my journalistic friend, M. Noir—"

"Oh, come to think of it, you may save yourself the trouble; that other second has informed M. Noir."

"I might have known it. It is just like that Fourtou, who always wants to make a display."

At half-past nine the following morning the procession approached the field of Plessis-Piquet in the following order:

first came our carriage; then a carriage containing M. Fourtou and his second; then a carriage containing two poet-
orators who didn't believe in God, and they had funeral
orations projecting from their pockets; then a carriage containing the head surgeons and their cases of instruments;
then eight private carriages with consulting surgeons; then
a hack wih a coroner; then two hearses; then a carriage containing the head undertakers; then a train of assistants and
mutes on foot; and after these a long procession of camp
followers, police, and citizens generally. It was a noble turnout and would have made a fine display if we'd had thinner
weather. There was a thick fog.

There was no conversation. I spoke several times to my
principal, but he didn't seem to be aware of it, for he always
referred to his notebook and muttered, "I die that France
may live."

When we arrived at the field we paced off the thirty-five
yards and then drew lots for choice of position. This really
didn't matter much, considering the weather, but it was part
of the code.

When I asked Gambetta if he was ready, he spread himself
out to his full width and said:

"Ready! Let the batteries be charged."

We considered it best to perform this delicate operation
with the help of a lantern, on account of the state of the
weather. Then we placed our men.

At this point the police noticed that the public had lined
themselves up on the right and left of the field. They re-
quested a delay while they put these poor people in a place
of safety. They ordered the multitude to take positions behind the duelists, and then we were ready.

The fog was getting worse, so it was agreed between myself and the other second that before giving the fatal signal

we would each deliver a loud whoop so the combatants could know each other's whereabouts.

By this time my principal had lost a good deal of his spirit, so I tried to buck him up. "Things aren't as bad as they seem," I told him. "Considering the size of the weapons, the fact that only one shot is allowed, the distance, the solidity of the fog, and the added fact that one of the combatants is one-eyed and the other cross-eyed and nearsighted, it seems to me this conflict doesn't necessarily need to be fatal. You might both survive. So cheer up!"

M. Gambetta stretched forth his hand and said:

"I am myself again. Give me the weapon."

I laid it, all lonely and forlorn, in the center of his palm. He gazed at it and shuddered. "Alas, it is not death I fear but mutilation. Let the tragedy begin. Stand at my back. Do not desert me in this solemn hour, my friend."

I gave him my promise and helped him to point his pistol to the spot where I judged his opponent was standing, and told him to listen sharply and guide himself by the other man's whoop. Then I propped myself against M. Gambetta's back and shouted, "Whoopee!" This was answered from somewhere out in the fog and I shouted:

"One-two-three-*fire!*"

Two little sounds like spit! spit! broke upon my ear, and in the same instant I was crushed to the earth under a mountain of flesh. Bruised as I was, I was still able to catch a faint voice from above muttering:

"I die for . . . for . . . perdition take it, what *is* it I die for? . . . oh, yes—*FRANCE! I DIE THAT FRANCE MAY LIVE!*"

The surgeons swarmed around, probing, and applied their microscopes to the whole area of Gambetta's person and found nothing in the nature of a wound. Then the two gladiators fell on each other's neck, with floods of proud and happy tears. The other second embraced me. Everybody cried and embraced and congratulated everybody else.

When the commotion had subsided somewhat, the surgeons held a consultation and after a good deal of debate decided that with proper care and nursing there was reason to believe I would survive my injuries. My internal hurts were the most serious, since it was apparent that a broken rib had penetrated my left lung, and that many of my organs had been pressed out so far to one side or the other, it was doubtful if they would ever learn to perform their functions again in such remote localities. Then they set my left arm in two places, pulled my right hip into its socket again, and re-elevated my nose. I was the object of great interest and admiration, and many sincere and warm-hearted people had themselves introduced to me, and said they were proud to know the only man who'd been hurt in a French duel in forty years.

I was placed in an ambulance at the head of the procession and marched into Paris, the most conspicuous figure in the great spectacle, and deposited in the hospital.

The cross of the Legion of Honor has been conferred on me. However, few escape that distinction.

I have no complaints to make against anyone. I acted for myself and I can stand the consequences. Without boasting, I think I can say I am not afraid to stand before a modern French duellist, but as long as I keep in my right mind I will never consent to stand behind one again.[9]

I see by this morning's newspaper that Teddy Roosevelt is still off on that bear hunt. I do wish he would stay home once in a while, so he could be found when needed.

Teddy and his Rough Riders and the infantry and artillery

have spent three weeks now chasing that bear all over the state of Louisiana—if it was a bear. Some say it was a cow. There were eye witnesses that testified that it was a bear, but they were all White House domestics, all under wages to the Great Hunter. And when a witness is in that condition, it makes his testimony doubtful.

I am sure the President honestly thinks it was a bear, but the evidence that it was a cow is overwhelming. It acted just as a cow would act when in trouble. It even left a cow track behind, which is what any cow would do, in distress. Or at any other time, if it knew a President of the United States was after it. When her strength was exhausted and she could drag herself no further, she did as any other despairing cow would have done—she stopped in an open spot, fifty feet wide, and humbly faced the President, with the tears running down her cheeks, and said to him, "Have pity, sir! Spare me! I am alone, you are many. I have no weapon but my helplessness, you are a walking arsenal. Have pity, sir—there is no heroism in killing an exhausted cow."

A grown person would have milked the cow and let her go. But nothing would do this lad but he must bag her. He is still only fourteen years old after living half a century.

Well, that exploit will take a good deal of shine out of the Twelve Labors of Hercules.[10]

Now let me bring you a selection from *The Gilded Age*. It concerns the case of a Senator who tried to buy out the opposing candidate at election time and got caught. It's an old story now, but it will bear retelling for the enlightenment of the young.

When the news broke the country was furious. Not because bribery was uncommon in our public life, but merely

because here was *another* case. Perhaps it did not occur to
the nation of good and worthy people that while they continued to sit comfortably at home and leave the true source
of our political power, the "primaries," in the hands of saloon-
keepers, dog fanciers, and hod carriers, they could go on
expecting "another" case of this kind and never be disappointed. However, they may have thought that to sit at
home and grumble would some day right the evil.

When the bombshell exploded the nation was naturally
excited, but Senator Dilworthy was calm. Calm, and up and
doing. What did he do first? Well, what would you do first,
after you had tomahawked your mother at the breakfast
table for putting too much sugar in your coffee? You would
ask for a "suspension of public opinion." That is what Senator
Dilworthy did and he got the usual amount of suspension.
Far and wide he was called a thief, a briber, a promoter of
railway swindles, a manipulator of temperance movements,
public charities, missionary enterprises, all for his private
benefit.

Then Dilworthy made another move. He moved to Washington and "demanded an investigation." Many newspapers
used language to this effect: "Senator Dilworthy's remains
have demanded an investigation. This investigation is likely
to be like all other Senatorial investigations—amusing but
not useful."

A committee was appointed to investigate. The newspapers commented again: "Under the guise of appointing a
committee to investigate the late Senator Dilworthy, the
Senate yesterday appointed a committee to investigate his
accuser—Mr. Noble. We are now reminded of a note which
we have received from the notorious burglar Murphy, in
which he finds fault with our statement that he had served
one term in the penitentiary and also one in the Senate. He

says, 'The latter statement is untrue and does me great in-
justice.' Further comment is unnecessary."

The Senate was roused by the Dilworthy case. One Senator jumped to his feet and said, "The presence in the Capitol
of such a creature as this man Noble, to testify against a
brother member of our body, is an insult to the Senate."
This was the same Senator who had been accused in the
public prints of selling his chances of re-election to his opponent for fifty thousand dollars and had not yet denied the
charge.

Mr. Noble appeared before the committee and testified
to the following effect:

He identified himself as a member of the legislature of his
state, a political enemy of Senator Dilworthy and bitterly
opposed to his re-election. He stated that Dilworthy had
come to the state capital and was reported to be buying
pledges of votes with money. He said that Dilworthy had
sent for him to come to his room at the hotel at night, where
the Senator urged him to vote for him. Noble declined. Dilworthy said that if Noble would vote for him he would make
him a Representative in Congress. Noble still declined to
vote, and said he did not believe Dilworthy was going to be
elected. Dilworthy showed him a list of men who would vote
for him—a majority of the legislature; gave further proofs of
his power by telling Noble everything the opposing party
had done or said in secret caucus; claimed that his spies reported everything to him, and that—

Here a member of the committee objected that this evidence was irrelevant. The chairman said, "Proceed—the committee can exclude evidence that does not bear upon the
case."

Noble said that his party would cast him out if he voted
for Dilworthy. Dilworthy said that this would be to his bene-

fit, because he would then be a recognized friend of his and this would exalt him politically and make his fortune. Noble said he was poor and it was hard to tempt him so. Dilworthy said he would fix that; he said, "Say you will vote for me and I will give you five thousand dollars—"

A member of the committee objected—said this stuff was all outside the case, and valuable time was being wasted. The chairman said the evidence need have no weight.

Mr. Noble said he told Dilworthy that five thousand dollars was too much to pay for a man's honor, character, and everything that was worth having. Dilworthy said he was surprised, asked what Noble's figure was. Noble said ten thousand would not be too little. Dilworthy said it was a great deal too much; he would not do it for any other man, but he had conceived a liking for Noble, and where he liked a man his heart yearned to help him; he was aware that Noble was poor, and the struggles of the poor always touched him. He then took from his pocket two thousand dollars in bank bills and handed them to Noble, and got another five thousand dollars out of his trunk—

A committee man jumped up and said:

"At last, Mr. Chairman, this shameless person has arrived at the point! By his own confession this man Noble has received a bribe, and did it deliberately! We have no need to hear the rest of his evidence."

The chairman said it would be better and more regular to proceed according to the usual forms.

Mr. Noble then concluded by saying that he had taken the money, gone straight to certain legislators, told them everything, and made them count the money. Then he had given the story to the newspapers. The rest of the ten thousand was to be paid the day after Dilworthy was elected.

Senator Dilworthy then took the stand. He wiped his

mouth with his handkerchief, adjusted his tie, and said that but for the fact that public morality required an example, he would beg that in Christian charity this poor misguided creature might be forgiven and set free.

He said that some instinct had told him from the beginning that this was a bad man, but his inexperience with such people had blinded him, and hence he had never dreamed that Noble's object was to undermine the purity of a United States Senator.

"It so happened," said the Senator, "that about the time in question, a poor young friend of mine, living in a distant town, out of my state, wished to establish a bank. He asked me to lend him the necessary money. I said I had no money just then, but would try to borrow it. The day before the election a friend said to me that my election expenses must be very large—especially my hotel bills—and offered to lend me some money. Remembering my young friend who wanted to start the bank, I said I would like a few thousands now, and a few more by and by. Whereupon, he gave me two packages of bills, said to contain two thousand and five thousand dollars respectively. I did not open the packages or count the money. I did not give any receipt for them. I made no memorandum of the transaction and neither did my friend.

"That night, that evil man Noble came troubling me again. He mentioned that he knew my young friend who wanted to start the bank, and that he had said he was very anxious to have seven thousand dollars now to begin his operations with. Noble wished to get the money and take it to him. So I gave him the two packages of bills. I took no receipt for them, and made no memorandum of the matter. This is all, gentlemen. To the absolute truth of every detail of my statement I solemnly swear; I pledge my honor as a Senator that

I have spoken but the truth. May God forgive this wicked man—as I do."

Mr. Noble spoke up. "Senator Dilworthy, your bank account shows that you have always conducted your financial business through the medium of checks, and so kept a careful record of every moneyed transaction—up to that day. Why did you deal in greenbacks on this particular occasion?"

The Chairman said, "The gentleman will please remember that the committee is conducting this investigation."

Mr. Noble: "Then will the committee ask the question?"

Chairman: "The committee will. When it desires to know."

Mr. Noble: "Which will be in the next century, no doubt?"

Several committeemen: "Mr. Chairman, this is contempt!"

Mr. Noble: "Contempt of whom?"

"Of the committee! Of the Senate of the United States!"

Mr. Noble: "Then I am become the acknowledged representative of a nation!"

Mr. Noble was taken out of action by a Sergeant-at-Arms.

The statement of Senator Dilworthy naturally carried conviction to the minds of the committee. It was close, logical, unanswerable. It bore many internal evidences of truth. For instance, it is customary for businessmen to loan large sums of money in bank-bills instead of checks. It is customary for the lender to make no memorandum of the transaction. It is customary to lend nearly anybody money to start a bank with, especially if you don't have the money to lend him and have to borrow it from someone else. It is customary to hand a large sum in bank bills to a man you have just been introduced to—if he asks you to do it—to be conveyed to a distant town and delivered to another party. It is not customary to get a receipt from the man who is going to convey it to that distant town, or from the man in the distant town whom the other man is going to convey it to. It would be at least singular in you to say to the conveyor, "You might be robbed. I will deposit the money in my bank and send a check for it to my friend through the mail."

The committee rendered its verdict: "Not proven that a bribe had been offered and accepted." This exonerated both men, and the honor and dignity of the Senate was saved.

Senator Dilworthy was offered a grand ovation by his friends at home. They said that he was still good enough for them.[11]

One of the results of a long and notorious career is that you receive a great many requests for advice. I am often asked to speak before groups of young people, and advise them as to the proper approach to life; and I am always delighted to do that, for I have some things in my mind which I've often longed to say for the instruction of the young. Just a few simple rules which I want to pass along to you now, and suggest that you distribute about the neighborhood.

You always want to start out by saying: My dear young friends, always obey your parents. When they are present. Now this is the best policy in the long run because if you don't they will make you. Most parents think they know better than you do, and you can generally make more by humoring that superstition than you can by acting on your own better judgment.

Be respectful to your superiors, if you have any; also to strangers; and sometimes to other people.

If a person offends you and you are in doubt as to whether or not it was intentional, do not resort to extreme measures. Simply watch your chance and hit him with a brick; that will be sufficient. Then if you find that no offense was intended, come right out frankly and confess yourself in the wrong when you hit him; acknowledge it like a man. Say you didn't mean to. But always avoid violence. In this age of charity and kindliness the time has gone by for such things. Leave dynamite to the low and unrefined.

Go to bed early, get up early. Now this is very wise. Some authorities say you should get up with the sun. Some say get up with one thing and some with another. But a lark is really the best thing to get up with. It gives you a splendid reputation with everybody to know that you get up with the lark! And if you get yourself the right *kind* of a lark, and work him right, you can easily train him to get up by nine-thirty every time.

Now then, as to the matter of lying. My dear young friends, you've got to be very careful about lying, otherwise you're nearly sure to get caught; and once caught you can never again be in the eyes of the good and the pure what you were before. Now some authorities say that the young ought not to lie at all. Well, that's putting it pretty strong. Stronger than necessary, I'd say. Still, while I don't go that far I do maintain, and I believe I am right, that the young ought to be temperate in the use of this great art until such time as practice and experience have given them that confidence, elegance, and precision which alone can make the accomplishment graceful and profitable. Patience, diligence, painstaking attention to detail, these in time will make the student perfect! Why, you just think for a minute what tedious years of study went into the equipment of that peerless old master who was able to impose upon the whole world the lofty and ringing maxim, "Truth is mighty and will prevail!" the most majestic compound fracture of fact which any of woman born has yet achieved. For the history of the whole human race, as well as each individual's experience, is sown thick with evidence that a truth is not hard to kill; but that a lie told well is immortal.

Never handle firearms carelessly. The sorrow and suffering that have been caused by the heedless though innocent handling of firearms by the young is simply appalling.

I remember a case last summer in the house adjoining ours. There lived a little old grandmother, gray and sweet, one of the loveliest spirits in the land. She was seated at her work one afternoon when her young grandson crept in and got down a battered old gun that hadn't been touched for years, and was not supposed to be loaded. He pointed it at her, laughing and threatening to shoot. The poor soul ran pleading and screaming towards the door but as she passed him— he pulled the trigger!

Now he had supposed that gun not to be loaded. And he was right. It wasn't. So there wasn't any harm done. But it's the only case of that kind that I've heard of. So for heaven's sakes, don't meddle with old, unloaded firearms. They're among the most deadly, unerring things that have been created by man. You don't have to take any pains with them at all. You don't have to have any sights on the gun. You don't even have to take aim. Just pick out a relative and bang away and you're sure to get him. Why, a youth who couldn't even hit a cathedral at thirty yards with a Gatling gun can take up an empty old musket and bag his grandmother every time. Why, you just think for a minute what Waterloo would have been if one of those armies had been boys armed with old muskets not supposed to be loaded and the other army had been composed of their female relations. The very thought of it makes one shudder.

There are many sorts of books; but good ones are for the young to read. Now you remember that, my young friends. They are a great, an unspeakable means of improvement.

So be very careful in your selection; confine yourselves ex-
clusively to *The Innocents Abroad, Tom Sawyer, Huckleberry Finn,* and other works of that nature.

I hope you will treasure up these instructions which I've
given you and make them a guide to your feet and a light
to your understanding. Build your character thoughtfully
and painstakingly upon these precepts and by and by when
you've got it built you will be surprised and delighted to see
how nicely and sharply it resembles everybody else's.[12]

And now I want to tell you a story from *Huckleberry Finn.*
This is a book about a boy. Some of you have been boys and
the rest of you have had a good deal to do with boys.

Huckleberry Finn is a boy who lived a good many years
ago in the Mississippi River Valley. He was ignorant, un-
washed, insufficiently fed; but he had as good a heart as
ever any boy had. And he was the only really independent
person, boy or man, in the community, and for this reason,
I suppose, he was continually happy. We liked him. We admired him. We enjoyed his society; and since his society was
forbidden us by our parents, we enjoyed it all the more.[13]

Now in this book Huckleberry tells his own story, all by
himself.

"You don't know about me without you have read a book
by the name of *The Adventures of Tom Sawyer.* That book
was made by Mr. Mark Twain, and he told the truth—mainly.
There were some things he stretched, but mainly he told
the truth. Aw, that ain't nothing. I never seen anybody but
lied one time or another, without it was Aunt Polly or the
Widow Douglas.

"The widow she took me for her son and allowed she
would sivilize me. She cried over me and called me a poor

lost lamb, and she called me a lot of other names, too; but she never meant no harm by it. Then she put me in some of them new clothes and I couldn't do nothing but sweat and sweat and feel all cramped up. Pretty soon I wanted to smoke but the widow she wouldn't let me. She said it was a mean practice and warn't clean and I must try not to do it any more. Ain't that just the way with some people, though! They get down on a thing when they don't know nothing about it. She took snuff, too. Of course that was all right, because she done it herself.

"Her sister, Miss Watson, a tolerable slim old maid with goggles on, she took a set at me with a spelling book. She worked me middling hard for about an hour, and then the widow made her ease up. I couldn't stood it much longer. Then for another hour it was deadly dull, and I was fidgety. Miss Watson was all the time saying:

"'Don't put your feet up there, Huckleberry. Don't scrunch up like that, Huckleberry—set up straight. Can't you try to behave?'

"Then she told me all about the bad place and I said I wished I was there. She got mad then. But I never meant no harm. All I wanted was a change. All I wanted was to go somewheres. I warn't particular. She said she was going to live so as to go to the good place. Well, I couldn't see no advantage in going where she was going, so I made up my mind I wouldn't try for it.

"I'd been going to school about four or five months and I learned to read and write and say the multiplication table up to six times seven was thirty-five. I don't reckon I could ever get further than that if I was to live forever. Then one night I lit my candle and went up to my room and there sat Pap, his own self!

"He tore into me something awful for dressing up, and

putting on airs, and going to school. Then he took a dollar offin me and went downtown to get some whiskey.

"Along in the spring he ketched me one day and took me up the river to a little log cabin over on the Illinois shore and I never got no chance to run off.

"Pap was so handy with his hickory I couldn't hardly stand it. I was all over welts. He was meanest when he got to drinkin, which was most of the time. Once after he'd been drunk over in town and laid in the gutter all night he come home and told me how folks was saying there was going to be another trial to get me away from him and give me to the widow for my guardian. Then he got to cussing and says he'd like to see the widow get me.

"He took a swig or two and got sort of warmed up and went to ripping again. Whenever his liquor begun to work he most always went for the government. This time he says:

" 'Call this a govment! Why, just look at it and see what it's like. Here's the law a-standing ready to take a man's son away from him—a man's own son, which he has had all the trouble and all the anxiety and all the expense of raising. Yes, and just when that man has got that son all raised up and ready to go to work and do suthin' for *him*, and give him a rest, why, the law up and goes for him! And they call *that* govment! A man can't get his rights in a govment like this.

" 'Why, looky here. There was a free nigger over there from Ohio—a mulatter, most as white as a white man, and he had the whitest shirt on you ever see, too; and the shiniest hat; and there ain't a man in that town that's got as fine clothes as what he had; and he had a gold watch and a chain, and a silverheaded cane—the awfulest old grayheaded nabob in the state. And what do you think? Why, they said he was a p'fessor in a college, and could talk all kind of languages, and knowed everything. Haw. And that ain't the

wust! They said he could *vote* when he was at home. Well,
that let me out! Thinks I, what's this country a-coming to?
It was 'lection day and I was just about to go and vote myself
if I warn't too drunk to get there; but when they told me
there was a state in this country where they'd let that nigger
vote, I drawed out. I says I'll never vote again. Them's the
very words I said; they all heard me. And the country may
rot for all me—I'll never vote ag'in as long as I live.'

"Pap was a-going on so he never noticed where his old
limber legs was taking him to, so he went head-over-heels
over a tub of salt pork and barked both shins; and the rest of
his speech was all the hottest kind of language—mostly hove
at the nigger and the government, though he give the tub
some, too. Then he let out all of a sudden with his left foot
and fetched that tub a rattling kick. But it warn't good judgment. That was the boot that had a couple of his toes leaking
out of the front end of it.

"I run off from Pap pretty soon after that, and I hid out
on Jackson's Island. That's where I met Miss Watson's Jim.
He says he run off too. Well . . . I promised I wouldn't tell
on him. I knowed I done wrong; I knowed people would call
me a low-down Abolitionist and despise me for keeping mum,
but I didn't care. I wasn't a-going back there again, anyways.

"Jim and me, we found an empty section of log-raft and
we set off down that river together. We run nights and laid
up and hid daytimes, and we just let that raft float wherever
the current wanted her to. We'd lay on our backs and smoke
our pipes, looking away in the sky. Not a cloud in it. The
sky looks ever so deep when you lay on your back in the
moonshine. I never knowed it before. And how far a body
can *hear* on the water, such nights!

"Once or twice of a night we'd see a steamboat slipping
along in the dark, and every now and then she'd belch a

whole world of sparks up out of her chimbleys, and they
would rain down in the river and look awful pretty. Then
she'd turn a corner and her lights would wink out and her
powwow shut off and leave the river still again. And by and
by her waves would get to us, a long time after she was gone,
and joggle the raft a bit. After that you wouldn't hear nothing, 'cept maybe frogs or something.

"I'd go to sleep, and sometimes Jim didn't call me when it
was my turn to stand watch. He often done that. And when
I waked up just at daybreak he'd be sitting there with his
head down betwixt his knees, moaning and mourning. I
never took no notice nor let on I knowed what it was about.
He was thinking about his wife and children away up yonder, and he was feeling low and homesick; because he hadn't
ever been away from home before in his life; and I do believe he cared just as much for his people as white folks does
for their'n. It don't seem natural, but I reckon it's so.

"He was often moaning and mourning that way nights,
when he judged I was asleep, and saying, 'Po' little 'Lizabeth!
Po' little Johnny! It's mighty hard; I spec' I ain't ever gwyne
to see you no mo', no mo'!' He was a mighty good nigger,
Jim was.

"But this time I somehow got to talking to him about his
wife and young ones. And by and by he says:

" 'What makes me feel so bad dis time 'uz bekase I hear
sump'n over yonder on de bank like a whack, er a slam, while
ago, en it mine me er de time I treat my little 'Lizabeth so
ornery. She warn't on'y 'bout fo' year ole, en she tuck de
skyarlet fever, en had a powerful rough spell; but she got
well, en one day right after dat she wuz a-stannin' aroun',
en I says to her, I says:

" 'Shet de do'.'

" 'She never done it; jis' stood dah, kiner smilin' up at me. It makes me mad; en I says ag'in, mighty loud, I says:

" 'Doan' you hear me? Shet de do'!'

" 'She jis stood de same way, kiner smilin' up. I was a-bilin'! I says:

" 'I lay I *make* you mine!'

" 'En wid dat I fetch her a slap side de head dat sont her a-sprawlin'. Den I went into de yuther room, en 'uz gone 'bout ten minutes; en when I come back dah was dat do' a-stannin' open *yit,* en dat chile stannin' mos' right in it, a-lookin' down and mournin', en de tears runnin' down. My, but I wuz mad! I was a-gwyne for de chile, but jis den, 'long comes de wind en slam dat do' shut, behine de child, ker-*blam!*—en, my lan', de chile never move! My breff mos' hop outer me; en I feel so—so—I doan' know *how* I feel. I crope out, all a-tremblin', en crope aroun' en open de do' easy en slow, en poke my head in behine de child, sof' en still, en all uv a sudden I say *pow!* jis' as loud as I could yell. *She never budge!* Oh, Huck, I bust out a'cryin' en grab her up in my arms, en say, Oh, de po' little thing! De Lord God Almighty forgive po' ole Jim, kase he never gwyne to forgive hisself as long's he live!'

" 'Oh, she was plumb deef and dumb, Huck, plumb deef and dumb—en I'd been a-treat'n her so!'

"We kept looking for Cairo, at the bottom of Illinois, where the Ohio River comes in. We said we'd sell the raft and get on a steamboat and go away up the Ohio amongst the free states, and then be out of trouble.

"Jim said it made him all over trembly and feverish to be so close to freedom. He says the first thing he'd do when he got to a free state he would go to saving up money and never spend a single cent, and when he got enough he would buy his wife, which was owned on a farm near Miss Watson! then they would both work to buy the two children; and if their master wouldn't sell them, they'd get an Abolitionist to go and steal them!

"Why, it most froze me to hear such talk! Jim wouldn't ever dared talk such talk in his life before—coming right out flat-footed and saying he would steal his children. Children which was owned by a man I didn't even *know*, a man who'd never done me no *harm*.

"You see, I begun to get it through my head that he *was* most free. And who was to blame for it? Why, me. It hadn't never come home to me before what this thing was that I was doing.

"My conscience got to stirring me up hotter and hotter until I says to it, 'Aw, let up on me, will you?—I'll paddle ashore at the first light . . . and *tell*.'

"Pretty soon one showed. Jim he got all excited because he thought it was Cairo. But I says, 'No! it might not be Jim. Let me paddle ashore in the canoe and see.'

"Well, he got the canoe ready for me, and give me the paddle, and I shoved out; and when I was about fifty yards off he calls out:

" 'Dah you goes, de old true Huck. De on'y white gentleman dat ever kep his promise to old Jim.'

"I just felt sick. There I was paddling off all in a sweat to tell on him, but when he says that it seemed to kind of take the tuck all out of me. And I warn't right down certain whether I was glad I started or whether I warn't. But I says to myself, 'I *got* to do it—I can't get *out* of it.'

"Right then along comes a skiff with two men in it, with guns, and they stopped and I stopped; and one of them says,

" 'What's that yonder?'

" 'A piece of raft.'

" 'You belong on it?'

" 'Yes, sir.'

" 'Any men on it?'

" 'Only one, sir.'

" 'Well, there's five niggers run off tonight up yonder, above the head of the bend. Is your man white—or black?'

"I didn't answer up prompt. I tried to, but the words wouldn't come. I tried for a second or two to brace up and out with it, but I see I was weaking, so I just give up trying. I says:

" 'He's white.'

"They went off.

"I knowed I done wrong. I see there warn't no use for me to learn to do right. A body that don't get *started* right when he's little ain't got no show.

"Then I says to myself, 'Hold on. If you'd a done right and give Jim up, would you feel better than what you do now? No,' I says, 'I'd feel bad—I'd feel just the same way I do now. Well, then,' says I, 'what's the use of you learning to do right when it's troublesome to do right and ain't no trouble to do wrong? And the wages is just the same.'

"I was stuck. I couldn't answer that.

"We talked considerable. Once we got to talking about kings and dukes and earls and such. And I told Jim about Louis Sixteenth that got his head cut off in France long time ago; and about his little boy the dolphin, that would 'a' been a king but they took and shut him up in jail, and some say he died there.

"Jim says: 'Po' little chap.'

" 'But some says he got out and got away, Jim, and come to America.'

" 'Dat's good! But he'll be pooty lonesome—dey ain't no kings here, is dey, Huck?'

" 'No.'

" 'Den *he* cain't git no situation. What he gwyne do?'

" 'Well, I don't know. Some of them gets on the police; and some of them learns people how to talk French.'

" 'Why, Huck, doan' de French people talk de same way we does?'

" '*No,* Jim; you couldn't understand a word they said—not a single word.'

" 'Well, now, I be ding-busted! How do dat come?'

" '*I* don't know, but it's so. I git some of their jabber out of a book. S'pose a man was to come to you and say Polly-voo-franzy—what would you think?'

" 'I wouldn't think nuffin. I'd take en bust him over de head—dat is, if he warn't white.'

" 'Shucks, it ain't calling you anything. It's only saying, do you know how to talk French?'

" 'Well, den why couldn't he say it?'

" 'Why, he *is* a-saying it. That's a Frenchman's *way* of saying it.'

" 'Well, it's a blame ridicklous way, en I doan' want to hear no mo' 'bout it. Dey ain't no sense in it.'

" 'Looky here, Jim; does a cat talk like we do?'

" 'No, a cat don't.'

" 'Well, does a cow?'

" 'No, a cow don't, nuther.'

" 'Does a cat talk like a cow, or a cow talk like a cat?'

" 'No, dey don't.'

" 'It's natural and right for 'em to talk different from each other, ain't it?'

" 'Course.'

" 'And ain't it natural and right for a cat and a cow to talk different from *us?*'

" 'Why, mos' sholy it is.'

" 'Well, then, why ain't it natural and right for a *Frenchman* to talk different from us? You answer me that.'

" 'Is a cat a man, Huck?'

" 'No.'

" 'Well, den dey ain't no sense in a cat talking like a man. Is a cow a man?—er, is a cow a cat?'

" 'No, she ain't either of them.'

" 'Well, den, *she* ain't got no business to talk like either one er the yuther of 'em. Is a Frenchman a man?'

" 'Yes.'

" '*Well*, den! Dad blame it, *why* doan' he *talk* like a man? You answer me *dat!*'

"I see it warn't no use wasting words—you can't learn Jim to argue. So I quit."

"It's lovely to live on a raft. We had the sky up there, all speckled with stars, and we used to lay on our backs and look up at them, and discuss about whether they were made or only just happened. Jim he allowed they were made, but I allowed they happened; I judged it would have took too long to *make* so many. Jim said the moon could 'a' *laid* them; well, that looked kind of reasonable, so I didn't say nothing against it, because I've seen a frog lay most as many, so of course it could be done. We used to watch the stars that fell, too, and see them streak down. Jim allowed they'd got spoiled and was hove out of the nest.

"One morning, when we was pretty well down the state of Arkansaw, we come in sight of a little one-horse town in a big bend of the river; so we tied up beneath some cypress trees and went on into town.

"The stores and houses was mostly shackly, dried-up frame concerns that hadn't ever been painted. They had little gardens around them, but they didn't seem to raise hardly anything in them but ash-piles, and old curled-up boots and shoes, and played-out tinware. There was generly hogs in the garden, and people driving them out.

"All the stores was along one street. You'd see as many as one loafer leaning up against every awning-post, and he most always had his hands in his britches, except when he fetched them out to lend a chaw of tobacco or scratch. What a body was hearing amongst them all the time was:

" 'Gimme a chaw 'v tobacker, Hank.'

" 'Cain't; I hain't got but one chaw left. Ask Bill.'

"Maybe Bill he gives him a chaw; maybe he lies and says he ain't got none. Some of them kinds of loafers get all their chawing by borrowing; they say to a fellow, 'I wisht you'd len' me a chaw, Jack, I jist this minute give Ben Thompson the last chaw I had'—which is a lie pretty much every time; it don't fool nobody but a stranger; but Jack ain't no stranger, so he says:

" '*You* give him a chaw, did you? So did your sister's cat's grandmother. You pay me back the chaws you've awready borry'd off'n me, Lafe Buckner, then I'll loan you one or two ton of it, and won't charge you no back intrust, nuther.'

" 'Well, I *did* pay you back some of it wunst.'

" 'Yes, you did—'bout six chaws. You borry'd store tobacker and paid back nigger-head.'

"All the streets was just mud, about a foot deep in some places. Hogs loafed and grunted around everywheres. You'd see a muddy sow and a litter of pigs come lazying along and whollop herself right down in the way, where folks had to

walk around her, and she'd stretch out and shut her eyes
and wave her ears whilst the pigs was milking her and look
just as happy as if she was on salary. Pretty soon one of those
loafers'd sing out, 'Hi! *so* boy! sick him, Tige!' and away that
sow would go, squealing most horrible, with a dog or two
swinging to each ear, and three or four dozen more a-coming.
All the loafers'd get up and watch the thing out of sight, and
laugh at the fun and look grateful for the noise. Then they'd
settle back down again till there was a dog-fight. There
couldn't anything wake them up all over, and make them
happy, like a dog-fight—unless it might be putting turpentine
on a stray dog and setting fire to him, or tying a tin pan to
his tail and see him run himself to death.

"There was going to be a circus in town that afternoon.
The nearer it got to noon, the thicker the wagons and horses
was in the streets, and more coming all the time. There was
considerable whiskey-drinking going on, and I seen three
fights. By and by somebody sings out:

" 'Here comes old Boggs!—in town for his little old monthly
drunk; here he comes, boys!'

"All the loafers looked glad. One of them says:

" 'Wonder who he's a-gwyne to chaw up this time. If he'd
a-chawed up all the men he's ben a-gwyne to chaw up in the
last twenty year he'd have considerable reputation now.'

"Another one says, 'I wisht old Bogg'd threaten me, 'cuz
then I'd know I warn't gwyne to die for a thousan' year.'

"Boggs comes a-tearing along on his horse, whooping and
yelling like an Injun, and singing out:

" 'Cler the track, thar. I'm on the waw-path, and the price
uv coffins is a-gwyne to raise.'

"He was drunk, of course, and weaving about in his saddle.
Everybody yelled at him and sassed him, and he sassed back,
and said he'd attend to them and lay them out in their

regular turns, but he couldn't wait now because he'd come to town to kill old Colonel Sherburn, and his motto was, 'Meat first, and spoon vittles to top off on.'

"He see me, and rode up and says:

" 'Whar'd you come f'm, boy? You prepared to die?'

"Then he rode on. I was scared, but a man says:

" 'He don't mean nothing; he's always a-carryin' on like that when he's drunk. He's the best-naturedest old fool in Arkansaw—never hurt nobody, drunk nor sober.'

"Boggs rode up before the biggest store in town, and bent his head down so he could see under the awning and yells:

" 'Come out here, Sherburn! You're the houn' I'm after. Come out and meet the man you've swindled.'

"He went on, calling Sherburn everything he could lay his tongue to. By and by a proud-looking man about fifty-five—and he was a heap the best-dressed man in that town, too—steps out of the store, and the crowd drops back on each side to let him come. He says to Boggs, mighty ca'm and slow:

" 'I'm tired of this, but I'll endure it till one o'clock. One o'clock, mind—no longer. If you open your mouth against me only once after that time you can't travel so far but I will find you.'

"Then he turns and goes in. The crowd looked mighty sober; nobody stirred, and there warn't no more laughing. Some men crowded around Boggs and tried to get him to shut up, but he wouldn't; they told him it would be one o'clock in about fifteen minutes, and so he *must* go home. But it didn't do no good. He went on cussing Sherburn with all his might, and throwed his hat down in the mud and rode over it, and pretty soon away he went a-raging down the street again, with his gray hair a-flying. Somebody says:

" 'Go for his daughter!—quick; sometimes he'll listen to her.'

"Somebody started on the run. Then, in about ten minutes here comes Boggs again, but not on his horse. He was a-reeling across the street towards me, with a friend on both sides of him, hurrying him along. He was quiet and looked uneasy; and he warn't hanging back any, but was doing some of the hurrying himself. Somebody sings out:

" 'Boggs!'

"It was that Colonel Sherburn. He was standing perfectly still in the street, and had a pistol raised in his right hand—not aiming it, but holding it out with the barrel tilted up towards the sky. That same second I see a young girl coming on the run, and two men with her. Boggs and his friends turned round to see who called him, and when they see the pistol the men jumped to one side, and the pistol-barrel come down slow and steady to a level—both barrels cocked. Boggs throws up both of his hands and shouts: 'O Lord, don't shoot!'

"Bang! goes the first shot, and Boggs staggers back, clawing at the air—bang! goes the second one, and he tumbles backwards onto the ground, heavy and solid, with his arms spread out. That young girl screamed out and comes rushing, and down she throws herself on her father, crying, and saying, 'Oh, he's killed him, he's killed him!' The crowd closed up around them, with their necks stretched, trying to see.

"Colonel Sherburn tossed his pistol onto the ground, turned around on his heels, and walked off.

"They took Boggs to a little drugstore. Pretty soon the whole town was there, pushing and shoving to get at the window and have a look, but people that had the places wouldn't give them up, and folks behind them was saying all the time, 'Say, now, you've looked enough, you fellows; 'tain't fair for you to stay thar all the time, and never give nobody a chance; other folks has their rights as well as you.'

"I got a good place at the window, where I was close to him and could see in. They laid him on the floor and put one large Bible under his head, and opened another one and spread it on his breast; but they tore open his shirt first, and I seen where one of the bullets went in. He made about a dozen long gasps, his breast lifting the Bible up when he drawed in his breath, and letting it down again when he breathed it out—and after that he laid still; he was dead. They pulled his little daughter away from him, screaming and crying, and took her off. She was about sixteen, and very sweet and gentle-looking, but awful pale and scared.

"Everybody that seen the shooting was telling how it happened. One long, lanky man, with long hair and a big white fur stovepipe hat on the back of his head, and a crooked-handled cane, marked out the places on the ground where Boggs stood and where Sherburn stood, and the people following him around from one place to t'other and watching everything he done, and bobbing their heads to show they understood, and stooping a little and resting their hands on their thighs to watch him mark the places on the ground with his cane; and then he stood up straight and stiff where Sherburn had stood, frowning and having his hat brim down over his eyes, and sung out, 'Boggs!' and then fetched his cane down slow to a level, and says 'Bang!' staggered backwards, says 'Bang!' again, and fell down flat on his back. The people that had seen the thing said he done it perfect; said it was just exactly the way it all happened. Then as much as a dozen people got out their bottles and treated him.

"By and by somebody said Sherburn ought to be lynched. In about a minute everybody was saying it. They snatched down the nearest clothes-line and went swarming up toward Sherburn's house, a-whooping and raging like Injuns, and everybody had to clear the way or get run over and tromped on. Children and dogs was heeling it ahead of that mob, trying to get out of the way.

"When they got to Sherburn's house, somebody sings out, 'Tear down the fence!' There was a racket of ripping and smashing, and down she goes, and the front wall of the crowd begins to roll in like a wave.

"Just then Sherburn steps out onto the roof of his little front porch, with a double-barrel gun in his hand, and takes his stand, perfectly ca'm and deliberate, not saying a word. The racket stopped, and the wave sucked back.

"Sherburn never said a word—just stood there, looking down. The stillness was awful creepy. Sherburn run his eye slow along the crowd; and wherever it struck the people tried to outgaze him, but they couldn't; they dropped their eyes and looked sneaky. Then Sherburn sort of laughed; not the pleasant kind, but the kind that makes you feel like when you are eating bread that's got sand in it.

"Then he says, slow and scornful:

" 'The idea of *you* lynching anybody! It's amusing. The idea of you thinking you had pluck enough to lynch a *man!* Because you're brave enough to tar and feather poor friend-less cast-out women that come along here, did that make you think you had grit enough to lay your hands on a *man?* Why, a *man's* safe in the hands of ten thousand of your kind—as long as it's daytime and you're not behind him.

" 'I know you clear through. I was born and raised in the South, and I've lived in the North; so I know the average all around. The average man's a coward. Why don't your juries hang murderers? Because they're afraid the man's friends will shoot them in the back, in the dark—and it's just what they *would* do. So they always acquit; and then a *man* goes in the night, with a hundred masked cowards at his back, and lynches the rascal. Your mistake is, that you didn't bring a man along with you; that's one mistake, and the other is that you didn't come in the dark and fetch your masks. You brought *part* of a man—Buck Harkness, there—and if you hadn't had him to start you, you'd 'a' taken it out in blowing.

" 'You didn't want to come. But if only *half* a man—like Buck Harkness, there—shouts "Lynch him! Lynch him!" you're afraid to back down—afraid you'll be found out to be what you are—*cowards*—and so you raise a yell, and hang yourselves onto that half-a-man's coattail, and come raging up here, swearing what big things you're going to do. The pitifulest thing out is a mob. But a mob without any *man* at the head of it is *beneath* pitifulness.

" 'Now the thing for *you* to do is to droop your tails and go home and crawl in a hole. If any real lynching's going to be done it will be done in the dark; and when they come they'll bring their masks, and fetch a *man* along. Now *leave*—and take your half-a-man with you'—and he tossed his gun up across his left arm and cocked it when he says this.

"The crowd washed back sudden, and then broke all apart, and went tearing off every which way, and Buck Harkness he heeled it after them, looking tolerable cheap. I could 'a' stayed if I wanted to, but I didn't want to.

"I went to the circus, and it was just the bulliest one I ever see. Then I went back to the raft, where Jim was waiting, and we shoved out.

"The stars was just beginning to show and they was awful pretty. We lit up our pipes and didn't talk or say nothing til we was way below town. It was kind of solemn drifting down the big, still river, laying on our backs, looking up at the stars, and we didn't ever feel like talking loud, and it warn't often that we laughed—only a little kind of a low chuckle. We said there just warn't no home like a raft, after all." [14]

And so Missouri has fallen, that great state! Certain of her children have joined the lynchers, and to the dwellers in the four corners of the earth we are "lynchers" now, and ever shall be. For the world will not stop and think—it never does, it is not its way. It will not say, "Those Missourians have been busy eighty years in building an honorable good name for themselves; these hundred lynchers down in the corner of the state are not real Missourians, they are renegades." No, that truth will not enter its mind; the world will generalize from the one or two misleading samples and say, "The Missourians are lynchers." The considerable fact that there are two and a half million Missourians who are *not* lynchers will not affect their verdict.

Oh, Missouri!

The tragedy occurred near Pierce City, down in the southwestern corner of the state. On a Sunday afternoon a young white woman who had started alone from church was found murdered. For there are churches there. Although it was a region of churches and schools the people rose, lynched three negroes—two of them very aged ones—burned out five negro households, and drove thirty negro families into the woods.

I do not dwell upon the provocation which moved the people to these crimes, for that has nothing to do with the matter; the only question is, does the assassin take the law into his own hands? The Pierce City people had bitter provocation; but no matter, they took the law into their own hands, when by the terms of their statutes their victim would certainly hang if the law had been allowed to take its course,

for there are but few negroes in that region and they are without authority and without influence in overawing juries.

It has been supposed—and said—that the people at a lynching enjoy the spectacle and are glad of a chance to see it.
It cannot be true; all experience is against it. The people in
the south are made like the people in the north—the vast
majority of whom are right-hearted and compassionate and
would be truly pained by such a spectacle—and *would attend
it* and let on to be pleased with it, if the public approval
seemed to require it. We are made like that, and we cannot
help it.

It is freely asserted in print that the lynching impulse is
not the outcome of a spirit of revenge, but of a "mere atro-
cious hunger to look upon human suffering." If that were so,
the crowds that saw the Windsor Hotel burn down would
have enjoyed the horrors that fell under their eyes. Did they?
Many risked their lives to save the men and women who were
in peril. Why did they do that? Because *none would disap-
prove.* There was no restraint; they could follow their natural
impulse. Why does a crowd of the same kind of people in
Texas, Colorado, Indiana, stand by, smitten to the heart and
miserable, and by ostentatious outward signs pretend to enjoy
a lynching? Why does it lift no hand or voice in protest?

Only because it would be unpopular to do it, I think; each
man is afraid of his neighbor's disapproval—a thing which,
to the general run of the race, is more dreaded than wounds
and death. When there is to be a lynching the people hitch
up and come miles to see it, bringing their wives and children. Really to see it? No—they come only because they are
afraid to stay at home, lest it be noticed and offensively commented upon. We may believe this, for we all know how *we*
feel about such spectacles—also, how we would act under the

like pressure. We are not any better nor any braver than anybody else, and we must not try to creep out of it.

A lynch mob would *like* to be scattered; there are never ten men in it who would not prefer to be somewhere else— and would be, if they but had the courage to go.

When I was a boy I saw a brave gentleman deride and insult a mob and drive it away. Then, perhaps, the remedy for lynchings comes to this: station a brave man in each affected community to encourage, support, and bring to light the deep disapproval of lynching hidden in the secret places of its heart—for it is there, beyond question. Then those communities will find something better to imitate—and being human, they must imitate something.

Where shall these brave men be found? That is indeed a difficulty; there are not three hundred of them in the earth. If mere *physically* brave men would do, then it were easy; they could be furnished by the cargo. No, upon reflection, the scheme will not work. There are not enough *morally* brave men in stock. We are out of moral-courage material! We are in a condition of profound poverty. We have those two sheriffs down South who—but never mind, it is not enough to go around; they have to stay and take care of their own communities.

But if we only *could* have three or four more sheriffs of that great breed! Would it help? I think so. For we are all imitators: other brave sheriffs would follow; to be a dauntless sheriff would come to be recognized as the correct and only thing, and that dreaded disapproval would fall to the share of the other kind; courage in this office would become custom, the absence of it a dishonor. Then the mobs and the lynchings would disappear, and—

However. It can never be done without some starters, and

where are we to get the starters? Advertise? Very well, then, let us advertise.

In the meantime, there is another plan. Let us import American missionaries from China and send them into the lynching field. With 1511 of them out there converting two Chinamen apiece per annum against an uphill birthrate of 33,000 pagans per day, it will take upward of a million years to make the conversions balance the output and bring the Christianizing of the country in sight to the naked eye; therefore, if we can offer our missionaries as rich a field at home at lighter expense and quite satisfactory in the matter of danger, why shouldn't they find it fair and right to come back and give us a trial? The Chinese are universally conceded to be excellent people, honest, honorable, industrious, trustworthy, kindhearted, and all that—leave them alone, they are plenty good enough just as they are; and besides, almost every convert runs a risk of catching our civilization. We ought to be careful. We ought to think twice before we encourage a risk like that; for, *once civilized, China can never be uncivilized again*. We have not been thinking of that.

Well, we ought to think of it now. Our missionaries will find that we have a field for them. Let them look at the following telegram and see if they have anything in China that is more appetizing. It is from Texas:

"THE NEGRO WAS TAKEN TO A TREE AND SWUNG IN THE AIR. WOOD AND FODDER WERE PILED BENEATH HIS BODY AND A HOT FIRE WAS MADE. THEN IT WAS SUGGESTED THAT THE MAN OUGHT NOT TO DIE TOO QUICKLY, AND HE WAS LET DOWN TO THE GROUND WHILE A PARTY WENT TO DEXTER ABOUT TWO MILES DISTANT TO PROCURE COAL OIL. THIS WAS THROWN ON THE FLAMES AND THE WORK COMPLETED."

We implore our missionaries to come back and help us in our need. They have the martyr spirit; nothing but the martyr spirit can brave a lynching mob, and cow it, and scatter it. We ask them to read that telegram again, and again, and picture the scene in their minds, and soberly ponder it; then multiply it by 115 lynchings in 1900, and 88 thus far this year; place the 203 in a row, allowing 600 feet of space for each human torch, so that there may be a viewing room around it for 5000 Christian American men, women, and children, youths and maidens; make it night, for grim effect; have the show in a gradually rising plain, and let the course of the stakes be uphill; the eye can then take in the whole line of 24 miles of blood-and-flesh bonfires unbroken, whereas if it occupied level ground the end of the line would bend down and be hidden from view by the curvature of the earth. All being ready, now, and the darkness opaque, the stillness impressive—for there should be no sound but the soft moaning of the night wind and the muffled sobbing of the sacrifices— let all the far stretch of kerosened fires be touched off simultaneously and the glare and the shrieks and the agonies burst heavenward to the Throne.

There are more than a million persons present; the light from the fires flushes into vague outline against the night the spires of 5000 churches. Oh kind missionary, oh compassionate missionary, leave China! Come home and convert these Christians! [15]

There is a familiar old maxim which assures us that Man is the noblest work of God. Who found that out? [16]

It is a curious and interesting invention, the Human Race.[17] Etiquette requires that we admire it.[18] And the pulpit has always been fond of referring to us as "the Chief Love and Delight of God!" Why, land, it's just the way I feel about it myself, even when dry. And when I'm not dry, why, even those warm words aren't nearly warm enough to describe what I am feeling, when I am holding onto something and blinking affectionately at myself in the glass, and recollecting that I am IT! [19]

It is strange and fine, nature's lavish generosities to her creatures; that is, to all of them except Man. For those that fly she has provided a home which is nobly spacious, a home which is forty miles high and envelops the whole globe and has not an obstruction in it; for those that swim she has provided a more than imperial domain, a domain which is miles deep and covers four-fifths of the globe. As for man, she has cut him off with the thin skin streched over the remaining one-fifth. The naked bones stick up through it in most places. On one half of this domain he can raise snow, ice, sand, rocks and nothing else; so that Man's inheritance really consists of but a single fifth of the family estate, and out of it he has to grub hard to get enough to keep him alive, and provide kings, and soldiers, and powder to extend the Blessings of Civilization with.

Yet Man, in his simplicity and complacency and inability to cipher, thinks that nature regards him as the most important member of the family—in fact, the favorite. It must occur to even his dull head sometimes that she has a curious way of showing it. [20]

I have heard it said—and by learned gentlemen—that the world was created for Man; that all these millions of years have been just a preparation for him. Well, I don't think we ought to decide too soon about it; not until all the returns are in.

Of course, he must have been a fine boy, that first prehistoric man. Just think of the style of him, how he must have lorded it over the other creatures, walking on his hind legs, waving his arms, practising for the pulpit.

But first God had to make the oyster. Now you can't make an oyster out of nothing. You've got to start with a vast variety of invertebrates: belemnites, trilobites, jebusites, amelekites, and that sort of fry; and put them in to soak in a primary sea, and observe and wait to see what will happen. Now some of them will turn out a disappointment, and will die out and become extinct. But all is not lost, for the amelekites will develop gradually into encrinites and stalactites and blather-skites, and one thing or another, and finally, after nineteen million years of this sort of thing, the first grand stage in the preparation of the world for man stands completed: the oyster is done!

Now an oyster has hardly any more reasoning power than a man has, so it's probable the oyster jumped to the conclu-sion that those nineteen million years were just a preparation for him. That would be just like an oyster. He had no idea that he was only an incident in a scheme, and that there was more to the scheme yet.

During the next fifty million years the fish and the reptile were made, and fossilized, so we'd have the evidence later.

Then came the pterodactyl, who thought all that prepara-tion had been intended to produce *him*, for there wasn't any-thing too foolish for a pterodactyl to imagine! Of course, you have to hand it to him—he was the triumph of his period. He wore wings and had teeth and was a mighty starchy-looking creature. But the progression went right along.

During the next thirty million years the bird arrived, and the kangaroo, and by and by the mastodon, and the giant sloth, and the Irish elk, and the old Silurian ass, and some people thought Man was about due.

But that was a mistake. For the next thing they know there

came a great ice sheet, and all those creatures escaped across the Bering Strait and wandered around in Asia and died—all except a few to carry on the preparation with. Then came six more ice sheets. Those poor orphans were chased up and down the earth, from weather to weather; they never knew what kind of weather was going to turn up next; and if they tried to settle down any place the whole continent suddenly sank from under them, and they had to make a scramble for dry land. They led that uncertain, strenuous existence for about twenty-five million years, always wondering what was going to happen next; never suspecting that it was all a preparation for Man—who had to be done just so; and then, by and by, the monkey came, and everybody could see at a glance that Man wasn't far off now. And that was true enough. The monkey went on developing for close upon five million years, and then he turned into a Man—to all appearances.

Well, it does seem like a lot of fuss and trouble to go through to build anything, impatient as the Creator must have been to see Man. And admire him. And I hope He's satisfied.

Man has just that one stupendous superiority: his imagination, his intellect. It makes him different from all the others. Those earlier animals didn't have it; and the monkey hasn't got it. Or he wouldn't be so cheerful.

And I've heard people talk about man being adapted to the earth, but I don't know how they arrive at that idea. He can't sleep out-of-doors without freezing to death, or getting rheumatism. He can't keep his nose under water for over a minute without being drowned. He can't even climb a tree without falling out and breaking his neck. Why, he's got to be coddled and housed and bandaged and upholstered to be able to live at all. He's a regular British Museum of infirmities.

He's always undergoing repairs. A machine as unreliable as he is would have no market at all.

The higher animals have few diseases; their main one is old age. But man starts in as a child and lives on diseases to the end, as a regular diet. He has mumps, measles, whooping cough, croup, tonsilitis, as a matter of course. Then, as he goes along, his life continues to be threatened at every turn by colds, coughs, asthma, bronchitis, influenza, pneumonia, carbuncles; and a whole catalogue of new ones that haven't even been discovered yet. Why, he's just a basketful of festering corruption, provided for the support and entertainment of microbes.

What's his appendix for? It has no value. Its sole interest is to lie in wait for stray grape seeds and breed trouble. What's his beard for? All nations persecute it with a razor. But nature always keeps him supplied with it, instead of putting it on his head where it ought to be. You seldom see a bald-headed man on his chin, but on his head. A man wants to keep his hair. It's a graceful ornament, a comfort, the best of all protection against the weather, and he prizes it above emeralds and rubies, and nature half the time puts it on so it won't stay.

Man isn't even handsome, as compared with the birds. And as for style, look at the Bengal tiger—that ideal of grace and majesty. Look at him! And then look at Man—that poor thing! The animal of the wig, the ear-trumpet, the glass eye, the porcelain teeth and silver windpipe—a creature that is mended and patched all over from top to bottom. If he can't get renewals of his bric-a-brac in the next world, what's he going to look like?

Well, you just have to remember that Man was made at the end of the week's work, when God was tired.[21]

We are always hearing about people who are going around seeking after Truth. I have never seen a permanent specimen. I have seen several entirely sincere people who *thought* they were permanent seekers after Truth. They sought diligently, cautiously, profoundly, with perfect honesty—until they believed that without doubt or question they had found the Truth. That was the end of the search. They spent the rest of their lives hunting up shingles to protect their truth from the weather. From that day forth, with their soldering iron in one hand and their bludgeon in the other, they tinkered its leaks and reasoned with objectors.[22]

We all have two opinions is my opinion. The one private, which we are afraid to express. The other—the one we use; the one we force ourselves to wear to please Mrs. Grundy, until habit makes us comfortable in it, and the custom of defending it presently makes us love it, adore it, and forget how pitifully we came by it.

It is our nature to conform. We wait to see how the drove is going, and then go with the drove.[23] A new style in women's dress appears, and the passers-by are shocked and the irreverent laugh. Six months later—nobody laughs. Why, if Eve should come again, in her ripe renown, and reintroduce her quaint styles—well, we know what would happen. And we should be embarrassed, along at first.

Look at it in politics. We conform there because we can't bear to be in disfavor; we want to stand well with our friends, to be smiled on and welcomed; we want to hear those precious words, "He's on the right track!" Uttered perhaps by an ass, but still an ass of high degree; an ass whose approval is gold and diamonds to a smaller ass, and confers glory and honor, and membership in the herd. For those rewards many a man will dump his lifelong principles into the street, and his conscience along with them. We have seen it happen.

We all do no end of feeling and we mistake it for thinking. And out of this we get an aggregation which we consider a boon. Its name is Public Opinion. It is held in reverence. It settles everything. Some think it is the voice of God.[24]

Do I seem to be preaching? It is not in my line. I only do it because the rest of the clergy appear to be on vacation.[25]

There is a venerable proverb which says, "Children and fools always speak the truth." The deduction is plain: adults and wise persons never speak it.[26]

Once, when Mrs. Clemens came to our daughter Susy's room to hear her little prayer before retiring, she noticed the child was troubled. Susy explained that Miss Foote, the governess, had been teaching her about the Indians and their religious beliefs, whereby it appeared they had not only one god, but several. This had set Susy to thinking. And she had stopped praying. Then she qualified this statement by saying that she did not now pray "in the same way." Her mother said, "Tell me about it, dear."

"Well, mama, the Indians believed they knew, but now we know they were wrong. By and by it can turn out that we are wrong. So now I only pray that there may be a God and a heaven—or something better."

My reverence for this pathetic prayer has grown with the years that have passed over my head since then. Its untaught grace and simplicity are a child's, but the wisdom and the pathos of it are of all the ages that have come and gone since the race of man has lived, and longed, and hoped, and feared, and doubted.[27]

Act Three

When I was a boy, in Hannibal, we used to spend some part
of every year on my uncle's farm. There was another uncle
on that farm, Uncle Dan'l, a middle-aged slave whose sym-
pathies were wide and warm. And every night we children,
white and black, used to gather around Uncle Dan'l's hearth
and hear him tell those immortal tales which Uncle Remus—
Joel Harris—got together in a book, by and bye, and charmed
the world with. And I can feel again the creepy joy that
quivered through me when the time for the ghost story was
reached.[1]

We'd sit there on the floor, in front of the fire, with our
knees hunched up, hugging 'em; watching the flames leap-
ing up the chimney, watching the shadows dancing over the
walls, looking suspiciously in all the dark corners, listening
to the wind whistle around the edge of the house—and we'd
be frightened to death before he'd even begin. And then he'd
tell us the story of the Golden Arm![2]

"Once 'pon a time dey wuz a monsus mean man, en he live
'way out in de prairie all 'lone by hisself, 'cep'n he had a wife.
En bimeby she died, en he tuck en toted her way out dah
in de prairie en buried her. Well, she had a golden arm—all
solid gold, fum de shoulder down. He wuz pow'ful mean—

231

pow'ful; en dat night he couldn't sleep, caze he want dat golden arm so bad.

"When it come midnight he couldn't stan' it no mo'; so he git up, he did, en tuck his lantern en shoved out thoo de storm en dug her up en got de golden arm; en he bent his head down 'gin de win', en plowed en plowed en plowed thoo de snow. Den all on a sudden he stop . . . en say: 'My *lan'*, what's dat!'

"En he listen—en listen—en de win' say, 'Bzzz-z-zzz'—en den, way back yonder whah de grave is, he hear a *voice!*—he hear a voice all mix' up in de win'—cain't hardly tell 'em 'part—'Bzzz-zzz—W-h-o—g-o-t—m-y—g-o-l-d-e-n—*arm?*—zzz-zzz—W-h-o—g-o-t—m-y—g-o-l-d-e-n—*arm?*'

"En he begin to shiver en shake, en say, 'Oh, my! *Oh,* my lan'!' en de win' blow de lantern out, en de snow en sleet blow in his face en mos' choke him, en he start a-plowin' knee-deep towards home mos' dead, he so sk'yerd—en pooty soon he hear de voice agin, en . . . it 'us comin' *after* him! 'Bzzz—zzz—zzz—W-h-o—g-o-t—m-y—g-o-l-d-e-n—*arm?*'

"When he git to de pasture he hear it agin—closter now, en a-*comin'!* a-com-in' back dah in de dark en de storm— 'W-h-o—g-o-t—m-y—g-o-l-d-e-n—arm?!' When he git to de house he rush upstairs en jump in de bed en kiver up, head and years, en lay dah shiverin' en shakin'—en den way out dah he hear it *agin!*—en a-*comin'!* En bimeby he hear—pat—pat—pat—*hit's a-comin' up-stairs!* Den he hear de latch open, en he *know* it's in de room!

"Den pooty soon he know it's a-*stannin' by de bed!* . . . Den—he know it's a-*bendin' down over him*—en he cain't skasely git his breath! Den—den—he seem to feel someth'n *c-o-l-d,* right down 'most agin his head! . . .

"Den de voice say, *right at his year*—'W-h-o—g-o-t—m-y—g-o-l-d-e-n—*arm?*' " (*You must wail it out very plaintively and accusingly; then you stare steadily and impressively into the face of the farthest-gone auditor—a girl, preferably—and let that awe-inspiring pause begin to build itself in the deep hush. When it has reached exactly the right length, jump suddenly at the girl and yell, "YOU'VE GOT IT!")*

(If you've got the pause right, she'll fetch a dear little yelp and spring right out of her shoes. But you must get the pause right; and you will find it the most troublesome and aggravating and uncertain thing you ever undertook.) [3]

And then that wicked old rascal would send us up to bed! And I can remember how very dark that room was, in the dark of the moon, and how packed it was with ghostly stillness when I woke up by accident, away in the night, and forgotten sins came flocking out of the secret chambers of my memory and wanted a hearing; and I remember how ill-chosen the time seemed for that kind of business. [4] We were all Presbyterians back there in that little Missouri town, and we all knew that if a boy committed a sin it meant the extermination of the whole countryside, cattle and all. [5]

And I remember the bare wooden staircase in my Uncle's house, and the turn to the left above the landing, and the rafters and slanting roof over my bed, and the squares of moonlight on the floor, and the white, cold world of snow outside. I remember the howling of the wind and the quaking of the house on stormy nights, and how snug and cozy I felt under the blankets, listening; and I remember how the powdery snow used to sift in, around the sashes, and lie in little ridges on the floor and make the place look chilly in the morning, and curb the wild desire to get up—in case there was any.

I remember the raging of the rain on the roof, summer nights, and how pleasant it was to lie and listen to it, and enjoy the white splendor of the lightning, and the majestic booming and crashing of the thunder. It was a very satisfactory room; there was a lightning rod which was reachable from the window, an adorable and skittish thing to climb up and down summer nights when there were duties of a sort to make privacy desirable.

The life which I led there with my cousins was full of charm, and so is the memory of it yet. I can call back the solemn twilight and mystery of the deep woods, the earthy smells, the faint odors of the wild flowers, the sheen of rain-washed foliage, the rattling clatter of drops when the wind shook the trees, the snapshot glimpses of disturbed wild creatures scurrying through the grass—I can call it all back and make it as real as it ever was, and as blessed. I can call back the prairie, and its loneliness and peace, and a vast hawk hanging motionless in the sky, with his wings spread wide and the blue of the vault showing through the fringe of their end feathers.

I know the taste of maple sap and when to gather it, and how to arrange the troughs and the delivery tubes, and how to boil down the juice, and how to hook the sugar after it is made; also how much better hooked sugar tastes than any that is honestly come by, let bigots say what they will. I know how a prize watermelon looks when it is sunning its fat rotundity among pumpkin vines; I know how to tell when it is ripe without "plugging" it; I know how inviting it looks when it is cooling itself in a tub of water under the bed, waiting; I know the crackling sound it makes when the carving knife enters its end, and I can see the split fly along in front of the blade as the knife cleaves its way to the other end; I know how a boy looks behind a yard-long slice of that melon, and I know how he feels, for I have been there. I know the taste of the watermelon which has been honestly come by, and I know the taste of the watermelon which has been acquired by art. Both taste good, but the experienced know which tastes best. I know the look of an apple that is roasting and sizzling on the hearth on a winter's evening, and I know the comfort that comes of eating it hot, along with some sugar and a drench of cream. I know the delicate art and mystery of so cracking hickory nuts on a flatiron with a hammer that the kernels will be delivered whole, and I know how the nuts, taken in conjunction with winter apples, cider, and doughnuts, make old people's tales and old jokes sound fresh and crisp and enchanting, and juggle an evening away before you know what went with the time.

It was a heavenly place for a boy, that farm of my Uncle John's. In *Huck Finn* and in *Tom Sawyer Detective*, I moved it down to Arkansas. It was all of six hundred miles but it was no trouble, it was not a very large farm; five hundred acres, perhaps, but I could have done it if it was twice as large. As for the morality of it, I cared nothing for that; I would move a state if the exigencies of literature required it.

All the negroes on the farm were friends of ours, and with those of our own age we were in effect comrades. I say in effect, using the phrase as a modification. We were comrades, and yet not comrades; color and condition interposed a subtle line which both parties were conscious of, and which rendered complete fusion impossible. Uncle Dan'l was a faithful and affectionate good friend, ally, and adviser; his head was the best one in the negro quarter, and his heart was honest and simple and knew no guile. He has served me well these many, many years. I have not seen him for more than half a century, and yet spiritually I have had his welcome company a good part of that time, and have staged him in books under his own name and as "Jim," and carted him all around —to Hannibal, down the Mississippi on a raft, and even across

the desert of Sahara in a balloon—and he has endured it all
with a patience and friendliness and loyalty which were his
birthright. It was on the farm that I got my strong liking for
his race and my appreciation of certain of its fine qualities.
This feeling and this estimate has stood the test of 60 years
and more and has suffered no impairment.

In my schoolboy days I had no aversion to slavery. I was
not aware that there was anything wrong about it. No one
arraigned it in my hearing; the local papers said nothing
against it; the local pulpit taught us that God approved it,
that it was a holy thing, and that the doubter need only look
in the Bible if he wished to settle his mind—and then the texts
were read aloud to us to make the matter sure; if the slaves
themselves had an aversion to slavery, they were wise and
said nothing.

Along outside of the front fence ran the country road, dusty
in the summer time, and a good place for snakes; when they
were "house snakes" or "garters" we carried them home and
put them in Aunt Patsy's workbasket for a surprise; because
she was prejudiced against snakes, and always when she took
the basket in her lap and they began to climb out of it, it
disordered her mind. She never could seem to get used to
them; her opportunities went for nothing. And she was always
cold toward bats, too. And could not bear them; and yet I
think a bat is as friendly a bird as there is. My mother was
Aunt Patsy's sister and had the same wild superstition. A bat
is beautifully soft and silky; I do not know any creature that
is pleasanter to the touch, or is more grateful for caressing,
if offered in the right spirit. My mother was not a suspicious
person, but full of trust and confidence; and when I said,
"There is something in my pocket for you," she would put
her hand in but she always took it out again herself; I didn't

have to tell her. It was remarkable, the way she couldn't learn to like private bats.[6]

When I was a boy, helping to inhabit that little Missouri town, there was one day in every week which I dreaded: Sunday. On Sunday we went to Sunday school, in the company of other sufferers. I believe I learned at that early age what the week is for: it is to give time to rest up from the weariness of Sunday.[7]

Sunday meant that each of us boys would have to memorize five verses of scripture, and for this labor each got his reward —in small blue tickets, each with a passage of scripture on it; each blue ticket was pay for two verses of recitation. Ten blue tickets equalled a red one and could be exchanged for it; ten red tickets equalled a yellow one; for ten yellow tickets the superintendent gave a very plainly bound Bible to the pupil. Can you imagine the industry and application required to memorize two thousand verses and thus acquire ten yellow tickets and a Bible? And yet my sister had acquired two Bibles in this way; and a boy of German parentage had won four or five. He once recited three thousand verses without stopping; but the strain upon his mental faculties was too great and he was little better than an idiot from that day forth—a grievous misfortune for the school, for on great occasions, before company, the superintendent had always made this boy come out and "spread himself." The delivery of one of these prizes was a rare and noteworthy circumstance, and in *Tom Sawyer* I have related such an incident.

At the door of the church, Tom stopped and accosted a Sunday-dressed comrade:

"Say, Billy, got a yaller ticket?"

"Yes."

"What'll you take for her?"

"What'll you give?"

"Piece of lickrish and a fish-hook."

"Less see 'em."

Tom exhibited. They were satisfactory, and the property changed hands. Then Tom traded a couple of white alleys for three red tickets, and some small trifle or other for a couple of blue ones. He waylaid other boys as they came, and went on buying tickets of various colors ten or fifteen minutes longer. He entered the church, now, with a swarm of clean and noisy boys and girls, proceeded to his seat and started a quarrel with the first boy that came handy. The teacher interfered; then turned his back a moment and Tom stuck a pin in another boy.

In due course the superintendent stood up in front of the pulpit with a closed hymn-book in his hand and his forefinger inserted between its leaves, and commanded attention. This superintendent was a slim creature of thirty-five, with a sandy goatee and short sandy hair; he wore a stiff standing-collar whose upper edge almost reached his ears and whose sharp points curved forward abreast the corners of his mouth—a fence that compelled a straight lookout ahead, and a turning of the whole body when a side view was required; his chin was propped on a spreading cravat which was as broad and as long as a bank-note, and had fringed ends; his boot toes were turned sharply up, in the fashion of the day, like sleigh-runners—an effect patiently and laboriously produced by the young men by sitting with their toes pressed against a wall for hours. Mr. Walters was very earnest of mien, and very sincere and honest at heart; and he held sacred things and places in such reverence, and so separated them from worldly matters, that unconsciously to himself his Sunday-school voice had acquired a peculiar

intonation which was wholly absent on weekdays. He began
after this fashion:

"Now, children, I want you all to sit up just as straight
and pretty as you can and give me all your attention for a
minute or two. There—that is it. That is the way good little
boys and girls should do. I see one little girl who is looking
out of the window—I am afraid she thinks I am out there
somewhere—perhaps up in one of the trees making a speech
to the little birds. (There was an applausive titter.) I want
to tell you how good it makes me feel to see so many bright,
clean little faces assembled in a place like this, learning to
do right and be good." And so forth and so on. It is not
necessary to set down the rest of the oration. It does not
vary, and so it is familiar to us all.

The conclusion of the speech was received with a burst
of silent gratitude. The whispering, which had marred the
last third of the speech, had been occasioned by an event
which was more or less rare—the entrance of visitors. They
were given the highest seat of honor; and as soon as Mr.
Walters's speech was finished, he introduced them to the
school. One turned out to be a prodigious personage—no less
than the county judge—altogether the most august creation
these children had ever looked upon—and they wondered
what kind of material he was made of—and they half wanted
to hear him roar, and were half afraid he might, too. He was
from Constantinople, twelve miles away—so he had traveled
and seen the world—these very eyes had looked upon the
county courthouse—which was said to have a tin roof. The
awe which these reflections inspired was attested by the impressive silence and ranks of staring eyes. This was the great
Judge Thatcher. Young Jeff Thatcher immediately went forward, to be familiar with the great man and be envied by

the school. It would have been music to his soul to hear the whisperings:

"Look at him, Jim! He's a-going up there. Say—look! he's a-going to shake hands with him—he *is* shaking hands with him! By jings, don't you wish you was Jeff?"

Mr. Walters fell to "showing off," with all sorts of official bustlings and activities, giving orders, delivering judgments, discharging directions here, there, everywhere that he could find a target. The librarian "showed off"—running hither and thither with his arm full of books and making a deal of the splutter and fuss that insect authority delights in. The young lady teachers "showed off"—bending sweetly over pupils that were lately being boxed, lifting pretty warning fingers at bad little boys, and patting good ones lovingly—and most of the teachers found business up at the library, by the pulpit; and it was business that frequently had to be done over again two or three times (with much seeming vexation). The little girls "showed off" in various ways, and the little boys "showed off" with such diligence that the air was thick with paper wads and the murmur of scufflings. And above it all the great man sat and beamed a majestic judicial smile upon all the house, and warmed himself in the sun of his own grandeur—for he was "showing off," too.

There was only one thing wanting, to make Mr. Walters's ecstasy complete, and that was a chance to deliver a Bible prize and exhibit a prodigy. Several pupils had a few yellow tickets, but none had enough—he had been around among the star pupils inquiring. He would have given worlds, now, to have that German lad back again with a sound mind.

And now at this moment, when hope was dead, Tom Sawyer came forward with nine yellow tickets, nine red tickets, and ten blue ones, and demanded a Bible. This was a thunderbolt out of a clear sky. Walters was not expecting an application from this source for the next ten years. But there was no getting around it—here were the certified checks, and they were good for their face. Tom was therefore elevated to a place with the Judge and the other elect, and the great news was announced from headquarters. It was the most stunning surprise of the decade, and so profound was the sensation that it lifted the new hero up to the judicial one's altitude, and the school had two marvels to gaze upon in place of one. The boys were all eaten up with envy—but those that suffered the bitterest pangs were those who perceived too late that they themselves had contributed to this hated splendor by trading tickets to Tom for the wealth he had amassed in selling whitewashing privileges. These despised themselves, as being the dupes of a wily fraud, a guileful snake in the grass.

The prize was delivered to Tom with as much effusion as the superintendent could pump up under the circumstances; but it lacked somewhat of the true gush, for the poor fellow's instinct taught him that there was a mystery here that could not well bear the light, perhaps; it was simply preposterous that *this* boy had warehoused two thousand sheaves of Scriptural wisdom on his premises—a dozen would strain his capacity.

Tom was introduced to the Judge; but his tongue was tied, his breath would hardly come, his heart quaked. He would have liked to fall down and worship him, if it were in the dark. The Judge put his hand on Tom's head and called him a fine little man, and asked him what his name was. The boy stammered, gasped, and got it out:

"Tom."

"Oh, no, not Tom—it is—"

"Thomas."

"Ah, that's it. I thought there was more to it, maybe.

That's very well. But you've another one I dare say, and you'll tell it to me, won't you?"

"Tell the gentleman your other name, Thomas," said Walters, "and say *sir*. You mustn't forget your manners."

"Thomas Sawyer—sir."

"That's it! That's a good boy. Fine boy. Fine, manly little fellow. Two thousand verses is a great many—very, very great many. And you never can be sorry for the trouble you took to learn them; for knowledge is worth more than anything there is in the world; it's what makes great men and good men; you'll be a great man and a good man yourself, someday, Thomas, and then you'll look back and say, It's all owing to the precious Sunday-school privileges of my boyhood—it's all owing to my dear teachers that taught me to learn—it's all owing to the good superintendent, who encouraged me, and watched over me, and gave me a beautiful Bible—a splendid elegant Bible—to keep and have it all for my own, always—it's all owing to right bringing up! That is what you will say, Thomas—and you wouldn't take any money for those two thousand verses—no indeed you wouldn't. And now you wouldn't mind telling me some of the things you've learned—no, I know you wouldn't—for we are proud of little boys that learn. Now, no doubt you know the names of all the twelve disciples. Won't you tell us the names of the first two that were appointed?"

Tom was tugging at a button-hole and looking sheepish. He blushed, now, and his eyes fell. Mr. Walters's heart sank within him. He said to himself, it is not possible that the boy can answer the simplest question—why *did* the Judge ask him? Yet he felt obliged to speak up and say:

"Answer the gentleman, Thomas—don't be afraid."

Tom still hung fire.

"Now," said the Judge, "the names of the first two disciples were—"

"DAVID AND GOLIATH!"

Let us draw the curtain of charity over the rest of the scene.[8]

But I was a good boy, you know—I was a very good boy. Why, I was the best boy in my school. I was the best boy in that little Mississippi town where I lived. The population was only about twenty million. You may not believe it, but I was the best boy in that state—and in the United States, for that matter.

But I don't know why I never heard anyone say that but myself. I always recognized it. But even those nearest and dearest to me couldn't seem to see it. My mother, especially, seemed to think there was something wrong with that estimate. And she never got over her prejudice.

And yet I was always reforming. Why, I remember the first time I ever stole a watermelon. Stole? Oh, no, I don't mean that. It was the first time I ever—withdrew a watermelon, retired it from circulation. It was the first time I ever *extracted* a watermelon—there's the phrase I want; it perfectly conveys my idea. Its use in dentistry connotes the delicate shade of meaning I'm looking for. You know, we never extract our own teeth; and it was not my watermelon that I extracted.

I extracted that watermelon from a farmer's wagon, while he was inside negotiating with another customer. I carried that watermelon to one of the secluded recesses of the lumberyard and there I broke it open. It was a green watermelon. Now, do you know when I saw that I began to feel sorry? It seemed to me that I had done wrong. I reflected—deeply;

I reflected that I was young; I think I was just eleven. And yet, though immature, I knew I did not lack moral advancement. I knew what a boy ought to do who had extracted a watermelon like that one.

I considered George Washington, and what action he would have taken under similar circumstances. And then I knew there was just one thing that was going to make me feel right again, inside; and that was restitution! I said to myself I will do that. And the minute I said it I felt the great moral uplift that comes to you when you have made a noble resolution. So I gathered up the biggest fragments, and I carried them back to the farmer's wagon, and I restored the watermelon. And I made him give me a good one in place of it, too.

And I told him he ought to be ashamed of himself, going around working off his worthless green watermelons on trusting purchasers who had to rely on him; I told him if he didn't reform I'd see to it that he got no more of my trade. Why, that man was as contrite as a revivalist's last convert. He promised he would never again carry another green watermelon if he starved for it; and he drove off—a better man.

When I think of what I did for that depraved farmer; and all I got out of it was a watermelon.[9]

And sometimes an incident would reform me. Once after I had run off from school, and come home late at night, I climbed in at the window of my father's law office to sleep on a bench there, because I had a delicacy about going home and getting thrashed. Just as I was becoming comfortable on that bench, a shaft of moonlight slipped in through the window and revealed to me a human hand upon the floor. I stood up to attention, and all my livers and lungs and everything fell right down into my legs. I watched that moonlight creep slowly along the arm until it revealed to me the face of a man, the eyes fixed and glassy in death!

I wasn't exactly scared but I was considerably agitated. I went away from there. I don't say I went away in any sort of a hurry, I simply went. I went out at the window; and I carried the sash along with me. I had no use for the sash; but it was handier to take it than it was to leave it, so I took it.[10]

But a boy's life is not all comedy. Much of the tragic enters into it: the drunken tramp who was burned to death in the village jail lay upon my conscience a hundred nights afterwards and filled it with hideous dreams, dreams in which I saw his appealing face pressed against the window bars with the red hell glowing behind him, a face which seemed to say to me, "If you had not given me the matches, this would not have happened; you are responsible for my death!"

I was not responsible for it. I meant him no harm, only good, when I let him have those matches. But mine was a trained Presbyterian conscience and it knew but the one duty—to hunt and harry its slave upon all occasions, particularly when there was no sense nor reason to it.

The shooting down of poor old Smarr in the main street at noonday supplied me with some more dreams. And in them I always saw again that grotesque closing picture, the great family Bible spread open on the profane old man's breast by some thoughtful idiot, rising and falling, rising and falling, adding the torture of its leaden weight to his dying struggle. We are curiously made. In all that gaping and sympathetic throng of onlookers there wasn't one with common sense enough to perceive that an anvil would have been in better taste there than the Bible. In my nightmares I gasped and struggled for breath under the crush of that vast book.

You see, my teaching and training enabled me to see deeper into these tragedies than an ignorant person could have done. I knew what they were for—down in the secret deeps of my troubled heart, I knew! And I *knew* I knew. They were inventions of Providence to beguile *me* to a better life. It seems curiously innocent and conceited now, but in those days I shouldn't have been surprised if Providence had killed off that whole community, trying to save an asset like me. It would have seemed just the thing; and well worth the price.

It's very true; I took all those tragedies to myself; and in every case I said to myself, with a sigh, "O—another one gone! And on *my* account! This ought to bring me to repentance; the patience of God will not long endure!" And yet, privately, I believed it would. That is I believed it in the daytime; but not in the night. With the going down of the sun my faith failed, and I repented. Repented and begged; begged like a coward, begged like a dog, in my own interest.

But my repentances could not stand the daylight. They shredded away in the glad splendor of the sun. In all my boyhood I don't believe I ever tried to lead a better life in the daytime. Nowadays, I should never dream of doing such a thing. But night—night still brings me many a deep remorse; and I realize that from the cradle up I have been just like the rest of the race: never quite sane in the night.[11]

I remember the Mississippi River. I used to be drowned in it regularly, every summer, and then be fished out and drained out and inflated and set going again by some chance enemy of the human race.[12] But it never seemed to bother my mother; she would only smile and say, "People born to be hanged are safe in water." [13]

When I was a boy, there was but one permanent ambition

among my comrades in our village on the west bank of the Mississippi River. That was, to be a steamboatman. We had transient ambitions of other sorts, but they were only transient. When a circus came and went, it left us all burning to become clowns; the first Negro minstrel show that ever came to our section left us all suffering to try that kind of life; now and then we had a hope that if we lived and were good, God would permit us to be pirates. These ambitions faded out, each in its turn; but the ambition to be a steamboatman always remained.

Boy after boy managed to get on the river. By and by, I ran away. I said I would never come home again till I was a pilot and could come in glory.

I became apprenticed to Mr. Bixby of the *Paul Jones*. He agreed to teach me the Mississippi River from New Orleans to St. Louis for five hundred dollars, payable out of the first wages I should receive after graduating. I entered upon the small enterprise of "learning" twelve or thirteen hundred miles of the great Mississippi River with the easy confidence of my time of life. If I had really known what I was about to require of my faculties, I should not have had the courage to begin. I supposed that all a pilot had to do was to keep his boat in the river and I did not consider that that could be much of a trick, since it was so wide.

One cannot easily realize what a tremendous thing it is to know every trivial detail of twelve hundred miles of river and know it with absolute exactness. If you take the longest street in New York, and travel up and down it, conning its features patiently until you know every house and window and lamp post and big and little signs by heart, and know them so accurately that you can instantly name the one you are abreast of when you are set down at random in that street in the middle of an inky black night, you will then have a tolerable notion of the amount and the exactness of a pilot's knowledge who carries the Mississippi River in his head. And then, if you will go on until you know every street-crossing, the character, size, and position of the crossing-stones, and the varying depths of mud in each of these numberless places, you will have some idea of what the pilot must know in order to keep the Mississippi steamer out of trouble. Next, if you will take half of the signs in that long street, and *change their places* once a month, and still manage to know their new positions accurately on dark nights, and keep up with these repeated changes without making any mistakes, you will understand what is required of a pilot's peerless memory by the fickle Mississippi.

A pilot must have a memory; but there are two higher qualities which he must also have. He must have good and quick judgment and decision, and a cool, calm courage that no peril can shake. Therefore pilots wisely train their cubs by various strategic tricks to look danger in the face a little more calmly.

Mr. Bixby served me in this fashion once, and for years afterward I used to blush, even in my sleep, when I thought of it. I had become a good steersman; so good indeed, that I had all the work to do on our watch, night and day. One matchless summer's day I was bowling down the bend above Island 66, brimful of self-conceit and carrying my nose as high as a giraffe's, when Mr. Bixby said:

"I am going below awhile. I suppose you know the next crossing?"

This was almost an affront. It was about the plainest and simplest crossing in the whole river. One couldn't come to any harm, whether he ran it right or not; and as for depth, there never had been any bottom there. I knew all this, perfectly well.

"Know how to *run* it? Why, I can run it with my eyes shut."

"How much water is there in it?"

"Well, that is an odd question. I couldn't get bottom there with a church steeple."

"You think so, do you?"

The tone of the question shook my confidence. That was what Mr. Bixby was expecting. He left, without saying anything more. I began to imagine all sorts of things. Mr. Bixby, unknown to me, of course, sent somebody down to the forecastle with some mysterious instructions to the leadsmen, another messenger was sent to whisper among the officers, and then Mr. Bixby went into hiding behind a smokestack where he could observe results. Presently the captain stepped out on the hurricane deck; next the chief mate appeared; then a clerk. Every moment or two a straggler was added to my audience; and before I got to the head of the island I had fifteen or twenty people assembled down there under my nose. I began to wonder what the trouble was. As I started across, the captain glanced aloft at me and said, with a sham uneasiness in his voice:

"Where is Mr. Bixby?"

"Gone below, sir."

But that did the business for me. My imagination began to construct dangers out of nothing, and they multiplied faster than I could keep the run of them. All at once I imagined I saw shoal water ahead! The wave of coward agony that surged through me then came near dislocating every joint in me. All my confidence in that crossing vanished. I seized the bell-rope; dropped it, ashamed; seized it again; dropped it once more; clutched it tremblingly once again, and pulled it so feebly that I could hardly hear the stroke

myself. Captain and mate sang out instantly, and both together:

"Starboard lead there! and quick about it!"

This was another shock. I began to climb the wheel like
a squirrel; but I would hardly get the boat started to port
before I would see new dangers on that side, and away I
would spin to the other; only to find perils accumulating to
starboard, and be crazy to get to port again. Then came the
leadsman's sepulchral cry:

"D-e-e-p four!"

Deep four in a bottomless crossing! The terror of it took
my breath away.

"M-a-r-k three! M-a-r-k three! Quarter-less-three! Half
twain!"

This was frightful! I seized the bell-ropes and stopped the
engines.

"Quarter twain! Quarter twain! *Mark* twain!"

I was helpless. I did not know what in the world to do.
I was quaking from head to foot, and I could have hung my
hat on my eyes, they stuck out so far.

"Quarter-*less*-twain! Nine-and-a-*half!*"

We were *drawing* nine! My hands were in a nerveless
flutter. I could not ring a bell intelligibly with them. I flew
to the speaking-tube and shouted to the engineer:

"Oh, Ben, if you love me, *back* her! Quick, Ben! Oh, back
the immortal *soul* out of her!"

I heard the door close gently. I looked around, and there
stood Mr. Bixby, smiling a bland, sweet smile. Then the
audience on the hurricane-deck sent up a thundergust of
humiliating laughter. I saw it all, now, and I felt meaner than
the meanest man in human history. I laid in the lead, set the
boat in her marks, came ahead on the engines, and said:

"It was a fine trick to play on an orphan, *wasn't* it? I suppose I'll never hear the last of how I was ass enough to heave the lead at the head of 66."

"Well, no, you won't, maybe. In fact, I hope you won't; for I want you to learn something by that experience. Didn't you *know* there was no bottom in that crossing?"

"Yes, sir, I did."

"Very well, then. You shouldn't have allowed me or anybody else to shake your confidence in that knowledge. Try to remember that. And another thing: when you get into a dangerous place, don't turn coward. That isn't going to help matters any."

It was a good lesson.[14]

The river was my school. On one trip I saw a little towhead, a small island, half a mile long, which had been formed during the past nineteen years. Since there was so much time to spare that nineteen years of it could be devoted to the construction of a mere towhead, where was the use, originally, in rushing this whole globe through in six days? It is likely that if more time had been taken in the first place, the world would have been made right, and this ceaseless improving and repairing would not be necessary now.[15]

When I stood in the pilothouse I was so far above the water that I seemed perched on a mountain. It was a sumptuous glass temple, offering a princely view of the great Mississippi, the majestic, the magnificent Mississippi, rolling its mile-wide tide along, shining in the sun. On the 4-o'clock watch, mornings, I could watch the summer sunrise on the river. Oh, that was enchanting! First, there is the eloquence of silence, for a deep hush broods everywhere. Then the haunting sense of loneliness, isolation, remoteness from the worry and bustle of the world. The dawn creeps in stealthily;

the solid walls of black forest soften to gray, and vast
stretches of the river open up and reveal themselves; the
water is glass-smooth, gives off spectral little wreaths of
white mist, there is not the faintest breath of wind, nor stir
of leaf.

Then a bird pipes up, another follows, and soon the pipings
develop into a jubilant riot of music. You see none of the
birds; you simply move through an atmosphere of song
which seems to sing itself. And then, when the light has
become a little stronger, you have one of the fairest and
softest pictures imaginable. You have the intense green of
the massed and crowded foliage near-by; you see it paling
shade by shade in front of you; upon the next projecting
cape, a mile or more off, the tint has lightened to the tender
young green of spring; the cape beyond that one has almost
lost color, and the furthest one, miles away under the horizon,
sleeps upon the water a mere dim vapor, and hardly sepa-
rable from the sky above it.

And all this stretch of river is a mirror, and you have the
shadowy reflections of the leafage and the curving shores
and receding capes pictured in it. Well, that is all beautiful;
but when the sun gets well up, and distributes a pink flush
here and a powder of gold yonder and a purple haze where
it will yield the best effect, you grant that you have seen
something that is worth remembering.[16]

Well, if I have seemed to love my memories of those days
on the river, it is no surprising thing; for I loved that profession far better than any I have followed since, and I took
a measureless pride in it. For this reason: a pilot on the
Mississippi, in those days, was the only unfettered and entirely independent human being that lived on the earth. I
hoped that I was going to follow the river the rest of my
days, and die at the wheel when my mission was ended; but

by and by the war came and commerce on the river ceased, and my occupation was gone.

I had to seek another livelihood. I became a silver-miner in Nevada, a gold-miner in California, a reporter, a foreign correspondent, an instructional torchbearer on the lecture platform, and I finally wound up a scribbler of books, and an immovable fixture among the other rocks of New England.[17]

I went back to the river, some few years ago, to refresh my memories of it, and I took my wife and little daughter along. And the first night out, as we lay silent in our bunks waiting for sleep, we heard the leadsman, crying through the night, "*MARK TWAIN. . . . MAARRK TWAAAIN.*" And my little daughter leaned over to me and whispered, "Papa! Don't you hear them calling you out there? Why don't you go out?" [18]

Maybe I ought to tell you how I stole that name. There was a man by the name of Captain Isaiah Sellers. He was a riverboat pilot, a fine man, a high-minded man, greatly respected both ashore and on the river. He was the patriarch of the craft, the only real and genuine Son of Antiquity amongst all the other pilots.

The old gentleman was not of a literary turn, but he used to jot down brief paragraphs of plain and practical information about the river, and sign them *MARK TWAIN*—two fathoms—and he'd give these paragraphs to the *New Orleans Picayune*. Thus far they contained no poison. But the old man's knowledge of the river was so wide and deep that the younger pilots resented it, and they used to chaff these "Mark Twain" paragraphs with unsparing mockery.

It so happened that one of them became the text for my first newspaper article. I burlesqued it broadly, very broadly.

I was a "cub" at the time. I showed my performance to some pilots and they eagerly rushed it into print. Well, it was a great pity—for it did nobody any worthy service and it sent a pang deep into the old Captain's heart. It laughed at him. It laughed at a man to whom such a thing was new and strange and terrible! I did not know then—though I do now— the suffering that a private person feels when he is for the first time pilloried in print.

Captain Sellers did me the honor to profoundly detest me from that day forth. When I say he did me the honor, I'm not using empty words. It was a distinction to be loved by such a man; but it was a much greater distinction to be hated by him; for he loved scores of people. But he didn't sit up nights to hate anybody but me.

He never again signed "Mark Twain" to anything. At the time the telegraph brought the news of his death, I was on the Pacific Coast. I was a fresh young journalist, and needed a *nom de guerre;* so I confiscated the ancient mariner's discarded one, and have done my best to make it remain what it was in his hands—a sign and symbol and warrant that whatever is found in its company may be gambled on as being the petrified truth. How well I have succeeded, it would not be modest in me to say.[19]

That was many years ago. Now I am seventy. Seventy! I am old. I recognize it, but I don't realize it. I wonder if a person ever ceases to feel young? I mean for a whole day at a time?[20]

Well, when you get to be seventy—actually I am older than that, but seventy is enough—after that there is too much risk.[21] When you get to be that age you are supposed to be able to sit up there on that seven-terraced summit and tell the rest of the world how you got up there. They all do it, you know, all these garrulous old people. They explain the process and dwell on the particulars with senile rapture. Well, I've been anxious to explain my system for some time, and now I have the right.

I think I've achieved my seventy years in the usual way: by sticking strictly to a scheme of life that would kill anyone else. Now I have just a few simple rules I try to follow:

I make it a point never to smoke more than one cigar at a time. I have no other restrictions. I never smoked any cigars with life-belts around them, either. They were always too expensive for me. I always smoked cheap ones. Reasonably cheap, that is. Sixty years ago they cost me four dollars a barrel, but my taste has improved lately and I pay seven now. Six or seven. Seven, I think. Yes, it's seven. But that includes the barrel.

I have never taken any exercise except sleeping and resting. I could never see any benefit in being tired.

As for diet, I've tried to be very strict about sticking to things that don't agree with me until one or the other of us got the best of it. Well, till recently I always got the best of it myself; but last spring I did stop frolicking with mince pie after midnight. Until then I'd always believed it wasn't loaded.

But the point I want to make is that you can't reach old age by another man's road. My habits protect my life but they'd probably assassinate you. You have to make up your own rules and then stick to them. That's not as easy as it sounds, either, because there's bound to be somebody trying to reform you, trying to take all the pleasure right out of your life and replace it with dreariness. But don't let them! If you can't make seventy by a comfortable road, don't go.[22]

Now that brings me to the final point: this reform business.

Why, it seems that whichever way you turn these days—somebody wants to reform you! I remember when they used to save up that sort of thing for Sundays, the idea being that if you used your morals too much on the weekdays they would get out of repair for the Sabbath.[23] Nowadays, this reforming is getting to be Big Business.

And that's a very discouraging fact for us unreformed people. Awfully discouraging . . . awfully discouraging.

Oh, I suppose it's a good idea to obey all the rules when you're young . . . just so you'll have the strength to break them when you're old.[24] But you cannot forget that experience is the best way to find out about something. A fellow who takes hold of a bull by the tail, once, is getting sixty or seventy times as much information as the fellow who hasn't. And anybody who starts in to carry a cat home by the tail is getting knowledge that's always going to be useful. Isn't ever likely to grow dim or doubtful. Chances are he won't carry the cat that way again. But if he *wants* to carry the cat that way, I say, let him! It isn't always easy to be eccentric.[25]

To tell the truth, I don't believe this reforming sticks very well anyway. I've always clung to the theory that you can straighten a worm out, but the crook is still in him, and only waiting.[26] My dear wife, God rest her soul, tried diligently for years to get me to give up profanity; and I tried, but I never had very much success with it.

All through the first ten years of my married life I kept a constant and discreet watch upon my tongue while in the house, and went outside for some distance when circumstances were too much for me and I was obliged to seek relief. I prized my wife's respect and approval above all the rest of the human race's, and I dreaded the day when she would discover that I was but a whited sepulcher, partly freighted with suppressed language.

But at last an incident exposed me. I went into the bathroom one morning to make my toilet, and carelessly left the door two or three inches ajar. It was the first time I had ever failed to take the precaution of closing it tightly. I knew the necessity of being particular about this, because shaving was always a trying ordeal for me, and I could seldom carry it through to a finish without verbal helps. This time I was unprotected and did not know it. I had no extraordinary trouble with my razor on this occasion, and was able to worry through with mere mutterings and growlings of an improper sort; but with nothing noisy or emphatic about them—no snapping or barking.

Then I put on a shirt. A button was missing. My temper jumped up several degrees in a moment and my remarks rose accordingly, both in loudness and vigor of expression. I flung up the window and threw the shirt out. It fell upon the shrubbery where people on their way to church could admire it if they wanted to. Still rumbling and thundering distantly, I put on another shirt. Again the button was absent. I augmented my language to meet the emergency and threw that shirt out the window. I was too angry—too insane—to examine the third shirt, but put it furiously on. Again the button was absent, and that shirt followed its comrades out of the window. Then I straightened up, gathered my reserves, and let myself go like a cavalry charge. In the midst of that great assault, my eye fell upon the gaping door, and I was paralyzed.

It took me a good while to finish my toilet. I tried to hope that Mrs. Clemens was asleep, but knew better. I could not escape by the window. It was narrow and suited only to shirts. At last I made up my mind to boldly loaf through the bedroom with the air of a person who has not been doing anything. I made half the journey successfully, but my confidence in my performance oozed steadily out of me as I went along. I had to stop in the middle of the room. I hadn't the strength to go on. I believed that I was under accusing eyes—that even the carved angels on the bedposts were inspecting me with unfriendly gaze. You know how it is when you are convinced that somebody behind you is looking steadily at you. You have to turn your face—you can't help it. I turned mine.

Against the white pillows I saw that young and beautiful face; and I saw the gracious eyes with something in them which I had never seen there before. They were snapping and flashing with indignation. I felt myself crumbling. I stood silent under that desolating fire for as much as a minute. Then my wife's lips parted, and from them issued my latest bathroom remark.

The language was perfect, but the expression unpractical, apprenticelike, absurdly weak, and unsuited to the great language. I had never heard anything so out of tune, so ill suited to each other as were those mighty words set to that feeble music. I tried to keep from laughing, for I was a guilty person in deep need of charity and mercy. I tried to keep from bursting, and I succeeded—until she gravely said, "There. Now you know how it sounds!"

Oh, then I exploded. I said, "Oh, Livy, if it sounds like that, God forgive me, I will never do it again." Then she had to laugh herself. Both of us broke into convulsions and went on laughing until we were exhausted.[27]

But there really ought to be a room in every house to swear in. It is dangerous to store up an emotion like that.[28] I could never get over the notion that in certain desperate and trying circumstances profanity furnishes a relief denied even to prayer.[29] So if I cannot swear in heaven, I shall not stay there.[30]

They probably won't let me in, anyway, from what my friends tell me. I remember once saying to our pastor, Joe Twichell, that I hoped to be cremated and he just looked at me and said, "Oh, I wouldn't worry about that if I had your chances." [31]

Well, I *would* like to see my old ancestor, Satan. I have no special regard for Satan, but I can at least claim that I have no prejudice against him. It may even be that I lean a little his way, on account of his not having a fair show. All religions issue Bibles against him, and say the most injurious things about him, but we never hear *his* side. We have only the evidence for the prosecution, and yet we have rendered the verdict. To my mind, this is irregular. It is un-English; it is un-American. It is French. Without this precedent Dreyfus could not have been condemned.

Of course Satan has some case, that goes without saying. It may be a poor one, but that can be said about any of us. As soon as I can get at the facts I intend to undertake his rehabilitation myself, if I can find an unpolitic publisher.

We may not pay him reverence, for that would be indiscreet; but we can at least respect his talents. A person who has for untold centuries maintained the imposing position of spiritual head of four-fifths of the human race, and political head of the whole of it, must have executive abilities of the loftiest order. I would like to see him. I would rather see him and shake him by the tail than any other statesman on the planet.[32]

And I probably will. Well, maybe it won't be so bad down there. When I think of the number of disagreeable people that I know who have gone to a better world ... I am sure it won't be so bad at all.[33] I always remember the poor fellow who tried diligently all his life to acquire heaven and when he finally got there the first person he met was a fellow he had been hoping all that time was in hell. He was so disappointed and outraged he inquired the way to hell and picked up his satchel and left.[34] So there you have it; Heaven for climate, and Hell for society.[35]

Now it is time to go. I came in in 1835, with Halley's Comet. It is coming again pretty soon and I expect to go out with it. It will be the greatest disappointment of my life if I don't go out with Halley's Comet. The Almighty has said, no doubt, now here are these two indefinable freaks—they came in together, they must go out together. Oh, I'm looking forward to that.[36]

But I cannot let you go without telling you something that is on my heart. You know, I cannot always be cheerful, and I cannot always be chaffing. I must sometimes lay the cap and bells aside and recognize that I am of the human race. And I want to tell you that I have received in this past year since my seventieth birthday hundreds of letters from all conditions of people, men, women, and children, and there is compliment, praise, and, above all, and better than all, there is in them a note of affection.

Praise is well, compliment is well, but affection—that is the last and final and most precious reward that any man can win, whether by character or achievement, and I am very grateful to have that reward.[37]

Many and many a year ago I gathered an incident from Dana's *Two Years Before the Mast.* It was like this: There was a presumptuous little self-important skipper of a coasting sloop, engaged in the dried-apple and kitchen-furniture trade, and he was always hailing every ship that came in sight. He did it just to hear himself talk and to air his small grandeur. One day a majestic Indiaman came ploughing by with course on course of canvas towering into the sky, her decks and yards swarming with sailors, her hull burdened to the Plimsoll line with a rich freightage of precious spices, lading the breezes with gracious and mysterious odors of the Orient. It was a noble spectacle! Of course, the little skipper popped into the shrouds and squeaked out a hail:

"Ship ahoy! What ship is that? And whence and whither?"

In a deep and thunderous bass the answer came back through the speaking trumpet:

"The Begum, of Bengal, one hundred and forty-two days out from Canton, homeward bound! What ship is that?"

Well, it just crushed that poor little creature's vanity flat, and he squeaked back most humbly:

"Only the Mary Ann, fourteen hours out from Boston, bound for Kittery Point, with nothing in particular!"

Oh, what an eloquent word, that "only," to express the depths of his humbleness! Now that is just my case. During just one hour in the twenty-four—not more—I pause and reflect in the stillness of the night with the echoes of your affection still lingering in my ears, and then I am humble. Then I am properly meek, and for that little while I am only the Mary Ann, fourteen hours out, cargoed with vegetables and tinware; but during all the twenty-three hours my vain self-complacency rides high on the white crest of your approval, and then I am a stately Indiaman, ploughing the great seas under a cloud of canvas and laden with the kindest words that have ever been vouchsafed to any wandering alien in this world, I think; then *I* am the Begum of Bengal, one hundred and forty-two days out from Canton, homeward bound! [38]

Good-night.

Epilogue

Humor is the great thing, the saving thing after all. The minute it crops up all our hardnesses yield, all our irritations and resentments slip away, and a sunny spirit takes their place.[39]

Mark Twain

Notes

ACT ONE

[1] Adapted from a verbatim report of Mark Twain's lecture "Roughing It" in Lansing *State Republican*, Dec. 21, 1871. Discovered and reprinted by Fred. W. Lorch in *American Literature*, XXII, 3 (Nov., 1950).

[2] Edited version of original line: "I was born modest; not all over, but in spots." From *A Connecticut Yankee*. New York: Charles L. Webster & Co., 1889, chap. XVI.

[3] Line, "I had scarcely in my lifetime listened to a compliment so beautifully phrased; or so well deserved," is adapted from a line in the "Lotos Club Speech," (1893) in *Mark Twain's Speeches*. New York: Harper & Bros., 1910, p. 310.

[4] Lawyer anecdote told to editor after a performance in St. Louis. Attributed to Mark Twain.

[5] Original line by editor suggested by one about critics in *Autobiography*. New York: Harper & Bros., 1924. Vol. II, p. 69.

[6] From *Mark Twain's Notebook*, ed. by A. B. Paine. New York: Harper & Bros., 1935, p. 237.

[7] Edited out of a remark in *Mark Twain in Eruption*, ed. by Bernard De Voto. New York: Harper & Bros., 1940, p. 311.

[8] Adapted from material in "The Last Lotos Club Speech," in *Mark Twain's Speeches*, 1910 ed., p. 25.

[9] Adapted from the "Lotos Club Speech," in *Mark Twain's Speeches*, 1910 ed., p. 310.

[10] From "The Last Lotos Club Speech," in *Mark Twain's Speeches*, 1910 ed., p. 25.

[11] Editor's original material.

[12] Edited from the "Seventieth Birthday Speech," in *Mark Twain's Speeches*, 1910 ed.

[13] Attributed to Mark Twain since Noah sailed in the ark. It may or may not be authentic.—Editor.

[14] Editor's original material.

[15] Edited from *Tom Sawyer*. Hartford: American Publishing Co., 1876, chap. XXII.

[16] Edited from *Following the Equator*. Hartford: American Publishing Co., 1897. Vol. I, chap. II, p. 22.

[17] Adapted from "Letters to Satan," in *Europe and Elsewhere*. New York: Harper & Bros., 1923.

[18] Edited from *Following the Equator*, vol. I, chap. II, p. 22.

[19] From "To My Missionary Critics," in the *North American Review* (April, 1901).

[20] From *Roughing It*. Hartford: American Publishing Co., 1871.

[21] From *Roughing It*.

[22] From *Roughing It*.

[23] From *Following the Equator*, vol. II, chap. XXIV.

[24] From *Roughing It*.

[25] From *Roughing It*.

[26] From "Information for the Million," included in *The Celebrated Jumping Frog of Calaveras County and Other Sketches*. New York: Charles H. Webb, 1867, pp. 144–52; also printed in the Virginia City *Daily Territorial Enterprise*, 1863.

[27] From "The Petrified Man," in *Sketches Old and New*. Hartford: American Publishing Co., 1890.

[28] From "Information for the Million."

[29] Edited from "Down the Rhône," in *Europe and Elsewhere*, p. 140.

[30] Editor's original material.

[31] From *Roughing It*.

[32] From *Roughing It*.

[33] Editor's original material.

[34] From *Daily Territorial Enterprise*, Jan. 7, 1872. Reprinted in *Mark Twain in Nevada* by Effie Mona Mack. New York: Charles Scribner's Sons, 1947. Also from review of lecture in Lansing *State Republican*, Dec. 21, 1871; reprinted by Fred W. Lorch in *American Literature*, XXII, 3 (Nov., 1950).

[35] From *Roughing It*, chap. XII.

[36] From *Mark Twain in Eruption*, ed. by Bernard De Voto. New York: Harper & Bros., 1940.

[37] From *Roughing It*.

[38] From *Mark Twain in Eruption*, pp. 220, 221, 222, 223.

[39] Edited from *Roughing It*, vol. II, chap. I.

[40] From an editorial in the Buffalo *Express*, 1870. Reprinted in *Europe and Elsewhere*.

[41] Mostly the editor's original material; partly edited from *Roughing It*.

[42] From *Mark Twain in Eruption*.

[43] From unidentified newspaper clipping about death of a Tammany leader. Reprinted in "Politics" in *Mark Twain at Your Fingertips* by Caroline Thomas Harnsberger. New York: Beechhurst Press, Inc., 1948.

[44] Edited from the "First Interview with Artemus Ward," in *Sketches Old and New*.

[45] Adapted from an anecdote told by Effie Mona Mack in *Mark Twain in Nevada*, pp. 237, 238.

[46] From articles written for the *Golden Era*, Sept. 25, 26, 27, 1863. Reprinted in *Mark Twain in Nevada*, pp. 238, 239.

[47] From "Universal Settlement Society," in *Mark Twain's Speeches*, 1910 ed. The anecdote, "I'm just moving again," included in this version of the poet story, was told to the editor.

[48] Edited from *Roughing It*, chap. XIX.

[49] From "Celebrated Jumping Frog of Calaveras," in *Sketches Old and New*.

[50] From the New York *Evening Post*, Sept. 16, 1880. Reprinted in *Mark Twain at Your Fingertips*, under "Uncle."

[51] Edited from *Roughing It*.

[52] From *Innocents Abroad*. Hartford: American Publishing Co., 1883. Vol. II, chap. XIV.

[53] Edited from *Roughing It*.

[54] From *Innocents Abroad*, vol. II, chap. XIV.

[55] Freely edited from *Roughing It*.

[56] Freely adapted from "Pudd'nhead Wilson's Calendar," in *Pudd'nhead Wilson*. Hartford: American Publishing Co., 1894, chap. VI.

[57] Freely adapted from *Roughing It*.

[58] Anecdote told to editor, attributed to Mark Twain.

[59] Editor's original material.

[60] Adaptation of "An Encounter with an Interviewer," in *Tom Sawyer Abroad; Tom Sawyer Detective and Other Stories*. New York: Harper & Bros., 1896.

[61] Words "Picnic on a gigantic scale" from *Innocents Abroad*, chap. I. The remainder is editor's original material.

[62] From "Statistics," in *Mark Twain's Speeches*, 1910 ed., p. 278.

[63] From *Innocents Abroad*, chap. XXVII.

[64] Adapted from quotation in *The Adventures of Thomas Jefferson Snodgrass*. Chicago: Pascal, Covici, 1928, p. x.

[65] Freely edited from *Autobiography*, vol. II, pp. 26, 106–112.

[66] From "Facts concerning the Recent Resignation," in *Sketches Old and New*.

[67] From *The Gilded Age*. Hartford: American Publishing Co., 1874, chap. XXIV, p. 225.

[68] From "After-dinner Speech," in *Sketches Old and New*.

[69] Edited from "Speech on Accident Insurance," in *Sketches Old and New*.

[70] From *Mark Twain, A Biography* by Albert Bigelow Paine. New York: Harper & Bros., 1912, vol. I, p. 149.

[71] From "Speech on Accident Insurance," in *Sketches Old and New*.

[72] Freely edited from "Independence Day," in *Mark Twain's Speeches*, 1910 ed.

[73] John Phoenix anecdote. Longer version of this story in *Mark Twain's Library of Humor*. New York: Charles L. Webster & Co., 1888.

[74] From "The Danger of Lying in Bed," in *The $30,000 Bequest and Other Stories*. New York: Harper & Bros., 1906.

[75] Edited version of "The Invalid's Story," in *Literary Essays*. New York: Harper & Bros., 1900.

[76] From the review of a lecture in the Washington *Post*, Nov. 25, 1883. In the Yale Collection of American Literature, Yale University.

[77] Freely edited from "The Awful German Language," in *A Tramp Abroad*. Hartford: American Publishing Co., 1880. Appendix D.

[78] Adapted from a line in a review in the Washington *Post*, Nov. 25, 1883. In the Yale Collection of American Literature, Yale University.

[79] Freely edited from "The Awful German Language," in *A Tramp Abroad*.

[80] From the New York *Sun*, Nov. 19, 1884. In the Yale Collection of American Literature, Yale University.

[81] Freely edited from "The Awful German Language," in *A Tramp Abroad*.

[82] Edited from "Taming the Bicycle," in *What Is Man? and Other Essays*. New York: Harper & Bros., 1917.

[83] From speech at banquet of the International Congress of Wheelmen (about 1884) in *Mark Twain's Speeches*. New York: Harper & Bros., 1923.

[84] From "Taming the Bicycle," in *What Is Man? and Other Essays*.

ACT TWO

[1] Adapted from *More Maxims of Mark*, ed. by Merle Johnson. Privately printed, 1927. Reprinted in *Mark Twain at Your Fingertips*.

[2] From *A Tramp Abroad*, chap. XXII.

[3] From *A Tramp Abroad*, chaps. II, III.

[4] From "At the Shrine of St. Wagner," in *What Is Man? and Other Essays*.

[5] Edited from *A Tramp Abroad*, chaps. IX, X.

[6] Anecdote told to the editor, attributed to Mark Twain.

[7] Freely edited from *A Tramp Abroad*, chap. X.

[8] From "At the Shrine of St. Wagner."

[9] From *A Tramp Abroad*, chap. VIII.

[10] Freely edited from *Mark Twain in Eruption*, 1940, pp. 7, 8, 10, 11, 12.

[11] From *The Gilded Age*, chap. LIX.

[12] Freely edited from "Advice to Youth," written about 1882, in *Mark Twain's Speeches*, 1923 ed.

[13] From *North American Review*, No. DCXX (Aug. 2, 1907). Reprinted in *Chapters from My Autobiography*.

[14] From *The Adventures of Huckleberry Finn*. New York: Charles L. Webster & Co., 1884.

[15] Edited from "The United States of Lyncherdom," written 1901, in *Europe and Elsewhere*.

[16] Edited from *Autobiography*, vol. II, p. 316.

[17] From *Mark Twain in Eruption*, 1940 ed., p. 81.

[18] From *More Maxims of Mark*.

[19] Freely edited from *Mark Twain in Eruption*, 1940 ed., p. 383.

[20] From *Following the Equator*, chap. XXVI.

[21] Freely edited from *Mark Twain, A Biography*, vol. IV, chap. CCLII.

[22] From *What Is Man? and Other Essays*, chap. IV.

[23] From *Autobiography*, vol. II.

[24] Freely edited from "Corn-Pone Opinions," in *Europe and Elsewhere*.

[25] From "About Play-Acting," in the *Forum* (Oct., 1898). Reprinted in *The Man That Corrupted Hadleyburg and Other Essays*. Hartford: American Publishing Co., 1903.

[26] From "On the Decay in the Art of Lying," in *Tom Sawyer Abroad; Tom Sawyer Detective and Other Stories*.

[27] Edited out of the *North American Review*, No. DC (Oct. 5, 1906). Reprinted in *Chapters from My Autobiography*.

ACT THREE

[1] Freely edited from the *North American Review*, No. DCX (Mch. 1, 1907). Reprinted in *Chapters from My Autobiography*.

[2] Editor's original material.

[3] From *How to Tell a Story and Other Essays*. New York: Harper & Bros., 1897.

[4] From *North American Review*, No. DCX (Mch. 1, 1907). Reprinted in *Chapters from My Autobiography*.

[5] From *Mark Twain in Eruption*.

[6] From *North American Review*, No. DCX (Mch. 1, 1907). Reprinted in *Chapters from My Autobiography*.

[7] Freely edited from *Adam's Diary*. Underhill & Nichols, 1893. New York: Harper & Bros., 1904, p. 29.

[8] Freely edited from *Tom Sawyer*, chap. IV.

[9] From "Morals and Memory," in *Mark Twain's Speeches*, 1910 ed.

[10] From *Innocents Abroad*, chap. XVIII.

[11] Freely edited from *Autobiography*, vol. I, pp. 130, 131, 133, 134.

[12] From *Life on the Mississippi*. Boston: Osgood & Co., 1883.

[13] From "Biographical Sketch," in *Literary Essays*.

[14] Freely edited from *Life on the Mississippi*, chaps. IV, VI, XIII.

[15] From *Life on the Mississippi*, chap. LI.

[16] Freely edited from *Life on the Mississippi*, chaps. IV, VI, XXX.

[17] From *Life on the Mississippi*, chaps. XIV, XXI.

[18] Adapted from anecdote in *Mark Twain—Wit and Wisdom*, edited by Cyril Clemens. New York: Frederick H. Stokes Co., 1935.

[19] Freely edited from *Life on the Mississippi*, chap. L.

[20] From *Mark Twain's Letters*, edited by A. B. Paine. New York: Harper & Bros., 1917.

[21] From *Following the Equator*, chap. XXIX.

[22] Freely edited from "Seventieth Birthday Speech," in *Mark Twain's Speeches*, 1910 ed.

23 From *Mark Twain's Notebook*, 1935 ed., p. 345. Everything before the line, "If you used your morals too much on the weekdays they would get out of repair for the Sabbath," is the editor's original material.

24 Editorialized version of a line, "Just so you'll have the strength to break them when you're old," from *Advance Magazine* (Feb., 1940), p. 2. "Mark Twain's friendship inspired a little girl to a successful career." Dorothy Quick, in *Mark Twain at Your Fingertips*.

25 Freely edited from *Tom Sawyer Abroad; Tom Sawyer Detective and Other Stories*, chap. X.

26 From *More Maxims of Mark*, p. 14.

27 Freely edited from *Autobiography*, vol. II, pp. 84, 87.

28 From *Mark Twain, A Biography*, vol. II, p. 767.

29 From *Mark Twain, A Biography*, vol. I, p. 214.

30 From *Mark Twain's Notebook*, 1935 ed., p. 345.

31 From *Life on the Mississippi*, chap. XLIII, p. 327.

32 From "Concerning the Jews," in *Literary Essays*.

33 Adapted from "Pudd'nhead Wilson's Calendar," in *Pudd'nhead Wilson*, chap. XIII, p. 123.

34 From *Mark Twain's Notebook*, p. 168.

35 From "Tammany & Croker," in *Mark Twain's Speeches*, 1910 ed.

36 From *Mark Twain, A Biography*, vol. III, p. 1511.

37 From "Books, Authors, and Hats," in *Mark Twain's Speeches*, 1910 ed.

38 From "The Last Lotos Club Speech," in *Mark Twain's Speeches;* 1923 ed.

39 From "What Paul Bourget Thinks of Us," in *Literary Essays*, p. 163.

List of Selections

(Since you have come hunting back here, it is only fair to provide a "list of selections" so that you, the curious reader, may identify the various "pegs" in my Mark Twain repertoire. These are the names I give them. For the authentic sources of each phrase, line, anecdote, or story, I refer you to the Notes.)

NEW HANOVER COUNTY PUBLIC LIBRARY

0047196

812   Holbrook, Hal
H   Mark Twain tonight!

Wilmington Public Library
Wilmington, N. C.

RULES

1. ~~Books marked 7 days may be kept one week.~~ ~~Books marked 14 days, two weeks. The latter~~ ~~may be renewed, if more than 6 months old.~~

2. ~~A fine of two cents a day will be charged on~~ ~~each book which is not returned according to the~~ ~~above rule.~~ No book will be issued to any person having a fine of 25 cents or over.

3. A charge of ten cents will be made for mutilated plastic jackets. All injuries to books beyond reasonable wear and all losses shall be made good to the satisfaction of the Librarian.

4. Each borrower is held responsible for all books drawn on his card and for all fines accruing on the same.

MLib